Production the TOC way

Production the TOC way
By
Eliyahu M. Goldratt

Distributed by: The North River Press,
P.O. Box 567, Great Barrington MA 01230
www.northriverpress.com

Contact Eli Schragenheim (elyakim@netvision.net.il) for technical assistance.

For information on Eliyahu Goldratt and his current projects
visit www.eligoldratt.com

<u>CONTENTS</u>

PRODUCTION THE TOC WAY WORKBOOK

PART ONE: THE PROBLEM
PART TWO: A SOLUTION

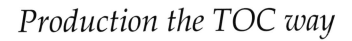

Production the TOC way

MY SAGA TO IMPROVE PRODUCTION

by Eliyahu M. Goldratt

In 1982, I was chairman and a major shareholder of a company ranked by Inc. Magazine as the sixth fastest growing company in the United States. And I was extremely frustrated.

Many dozens of clients had bought our production scheduling software and, guided by our associated education, had successfully implemented it. I was frustrated that we didn't have thousands of such clients. No, I don't think that I was greedy or overly ambitious. I had very good reasons to expect that every plant would embrace our package with open arms.

True, the underlying concepts of our offerings were quite revolutionary at that time. They flew in the face of accepted policies and procedures, but they were obviously correct . . . at least to me. More importantly, our software worked. I don't just mean that it didn't bump, or that it performed according to the written specifications, or that it was efficient in producing reports. It really worked. Most of our clients were willing to testify that using the software they were able to increase production while decreasing inventory. Many were willing to say that their pay back, on our not exactly cheap product, was less than six months. And we had reputable clients: RCA, GE, GM, Avco, Bendix, Westinghouse, Kodak, Philips, Lucas, ITT. . . .

And the market was primed. Every plant was busy installing a computer package—automation was the fad of the time. And the need was there. Like today, every production manager was struggling to increase throughput and improve due-date performance; many even started to pay attention to the desirability of reducing work-in-process. We were the only company that was providing a finite capacity

1

software that could really do it. So why was it so difficult to get more clients?

It wasn't for a lack of effort. Our thoroughly educated people* were constantly on the road, giving seminars, presentations, workshops, even doing pilot implementations. In spite of all these efforts our progress was painfully slow. I expected a tidal wave, and what was coming was, in my eyes, just a trickle.

Out of desperation, I decided that if conventional presentations were not effective in breaking the dam, maybe a non-conventional approach would. I had an idea: to convey my method through a novel about manufacturing. If people read about lawyers and doctors, why not plant managers? I started to work on THE GOAL.

Nobody liked it. Not even Jeff Cox, the writer that I hired. He hated it to the extent that he refused to share in the royalties and demanded to be paid cash, in full (as far as I know he didn't repeat this enormous mistake with Zapp!, the excellent book he co-authored later).

The most opposition came from my own people; most refused to read the drafts. I didn't blame them. I was the chief salesman, the prime presenter, the developer. I was the bottleneck, and here I was, wasting my time writing a novel. No, they didn't like it one bit.

I liked it. After thirteen long months of labor, it was finally complete. I was pleased with the results, and thought it was good. The publishers didn't think so. Not the two dozen or so I approached. The most polite rejection I got was from McGraw Hill: "Dr. Goldratt, if you'd like to write a book about scheduling the shop floor, we'd be delighted to be your publisher. If you want to write a love story,

---

* The education was not centered around the software, but rather on the cause and effect relationships that exist in manufacturing. I found that production plants are not as complicated as one might think. Besides production lines, all other plants can be categorized into only three configurations: A, V and T. Determine the configuration and you know the cause-effect relationships which govern the plant. This body of knowledge I developed in the early eighties and cast it into a two-week course. This education enabled my people to dazzle a client with their deep insight, a fact that contributed much to our success.

2

maybe we'll look at it. But a love story about manufacturing?? Forget it! It will never work. We don't even know which shelf to put it on!"

Larry Gadd, the owner of North River Press, was the only spot of light, but even he didn't really encourage me either. He claimed that we'd be lucky to sell the first printing (3000 copies), but since he personally liked the book so much, he would print it nevertheless. And he did. We gave one hundred bound galleys as gifts, and the snow ball started to roll.

It's a compliment for an author when people praise his book. It's an even bigger compliment when they recommend it to others. But the ultimate compliment is people buying the book, in quantities, to give as gifts. And that's exactly what happened. "We will not sell even 3000 copies..." What a joke!

Our prospect list exploded. It was quite amusing to watch the change in my own peoples' attitude toward the book. The enthusiastic response of their prospects embarrassed them to the extent that, finally, they read it. Within two months they all had amnesia - each of them claimed that he always was a big supporter of the idea of a novel. I didn't bother to argue.

Fan letters started to arrive; letters from plant managers attesting to the realism of the book, "THE GOAL is written specifically about our plant. We can even tell you the real names of the characters." Some even accused me of hiding in their factory.

It wasn't long before the letters started to detail actual results. One plant manager wrote, "Your book is not a novel anymore - now it's a documentary. We followed Alex Rogo's actions to the letter and we replicated his results exactly. Currently, the only difference between your book and my reality is that my wife didn't come back yet." Many letters included an invitation to come and visit, which I sometimes did.

The impact on me personally? It wasn't what one might expect. All of this threw me into the most difficult period of my life. I felt caught between a rock and a hard place. I almost gave up.

When I wrote THE GOAL, I tried to focus on the need to change the paradigm that governs industry. We knew that was the major stumbling block standing in the way of a plant reaching much better performance. To achieve the proper focus in the book, I down-played the role of a computerized scheduling package. Not that I thought that it was not needed. On the contrary, I thought that our software, or some variation of it, was a must for most plants.

By now the letters, and even more so the visits, forced me to face an unpleasant fact. Reality showed that the software, my cherished baby that I was so proud of, was an impediment to achieving results. The plants that were exposed only to THE GOAL and succeeded to put it to work, achieved better results and in a shorter time than our clients who had spent so much money on our software and education. How come?

It took me some time to figure it out, but at last I couldn't escape the simple explanation: the efforts to install the software distracted the plant people from concentrating on the required changes—the changes in fundamental concepts, measurements and procedures. How could we, with clear conscience, continue to persuade companies to buy our products?

You can imagine the magnitude of my dilemma. My responsibility to my shareholders and to my employees demanded that we continue business as usual. My responsibility to my clients and to myself demanded that we stop selling our main product.

I was frozen, but reality has a momentum of its own. When people start to have severe doubts about the validity of their product they cannot radiate confidence in it. And radiating confidence is essential to the sale of a revolutionary product. The manual implementation described in THE GOAL eroded our people's confidence in the absolute need for the software, and when they approached me for answers, I unavoidably increased their doubts. No wonder that in spite of the fact that prospects were now calling us, our actual sales went way down.

I was devastated. The software package in which I had invested almost ten years of hard work, the thing that I regarded as my biggest achievement, turned out to be hurting more than helping. My company, my pride and joy, was tumbling down, and the only apparent way to rescue it was to compromise on my integrity. Those were hard times. I think that the only things that kept me going were pride and inertia.

A few more months went by and reality tapped on my window, and then started banging on it, with another astonishing phenomenon. It was so strange that we couldn't believe our eyes.

Most readers of THE GOAL agreed with its message to the extent that they called it "common-sense." Nevertheless, they didn't implement it! They continued to ignore the constraints, they continued to try to improve everything they knew how to improve, they continued to justify investments based on cost calculations, they continued to make decisions based on product-cost impact, they continued to ignore the fundamental difference between a transfer batch and a process batch, they even continued to measure efficiencies and variances. And this was done even in companies where the president made THE GOAL mandatory reading! How come?

How come that even though it seemed everybody agreed with what is written in THE GOAL, only a handful of companies were actually implementing it? It was obvious that something was badly missing. What was it?

I started to question the people who were praising my book, listening very attentively to how they explained the lack of its rigorous implementation in their own plants. It wasn't long before the major obstacles standing in the way of putting THE GOAL to work become clear.

The list was surprisingly short:

1. Lack of ability to propagate the message throughout the company.

It's not easy to explain in ten minutes the message of THE GOAL. It's not easy to do it in an hour... or two...or eight. It's not easy to explain the message of THE GOAL, period. The alternative was to give a copy of the book. Alas, not all people read books, and those who do are sick and tired of management books.

2. Lack of ability to translate what they learned from the book into workable procedures for their plant.

Usually this obstacle was presented as, "our bottlenecks are constantly moving," or, "we have a unique situation." No, these are not pitiful excuses. These people were telling us the truth, as much as I didn't like to hear it. What they were alluding to was that I'd only done a partial job. In the book I'd exposed the fallacies of the existing paradigm in manufacturing; I'd revealed the essence of the needed paradigm (on those I'd probably done a good job) but I didn't provide the process of operating in the new paradigm. I provided examples, not a procedure. And examples are not always sufficient to extrapolate the needed procedures.

3. Lack of ability to persuade decision makers to allow the change of some of the measurements.

This last obstacle was more profound in plants that were part of large companies. This highlighted that I had done a sloppy job in explaining performance measurements.

So why didn't these obstacles block everybody? All the companies who made it based on the book alone had something in common: they all were led by a charismatic and very analytical plant manager. This person achieved the needed buy-in using mainly his/her charisma, and then their enthused group, using their experience and intuition, worked out the needed procedures.

I started to frantically develop the answers for the above obstacles—it was invigorating. Within less than three months we had the essentials; the precise verbalization of the need to change the measurements, and the rules of the logistical procedures – the Drum-Buffer-Rope and Buffer-Management. That was easy. What was less easy was teaching it to my people. They resisted the change in emphasis with all their might. The Sunday that I devoted to educating them to give the resulting new, one-day presentation, they called "Bloody Sunday."

But it was an unfair fight; I had the logic and they were less than two hundred. Not before long the enthusiastic response of the market caused a return of the amnesia epidemic. They all fell in love with the new presentation. Bob Fox helped me to turn that presentation into a book - THE RACE. Larry Gadd went out of his way to expeditiously provide it. This went a long way toward resolving the second and third obstacles. I turned my attention to solving the first one.

And once again I used the computer. No, not a modified scheduling package but using the computer in what it's so effective at - games. I started to develop addictive educational games which led people to invent the needed procedures. If there is something more powerful than a novel, it's a computer game. But it was too late. We'd run out of time.

Our shareholders were far from being pleased with the financial results of our company. From a money-making machine we had turned into a bottomless pit. When they realized that my plans did not include any real actions to boost our software sales, they decided that I had turned from an asset into a liability. They showed me the door. And then, one by one, they showed the door to our best people; they were "contaminated" by my ideas.

I founded the Avraham Y. Goldratt Institute, named after my late father, and we frantically developed the educational games. In less than two months, we were profitable. But much more importantly, we could deliver results to our clients at speeds that matched the story in THE GOAL. Life looked bright again.

I was careful not to repeat the same mistakes. This time we didn't have any external shareholders and in the incorporation papers it was clearly stated that the goal of the institute was "to generate and disseminate knowledge," and that our decisions were not going to be based on financial considerations.

During that period I verbalized what should have been the starting point; I verbalized the steps of the process of ongoing improvement—which I later published in the second, more extended, edition of THE GOAL.

These five focusing steps turned out to be extremely helpful. They helped our clients to constantly improve their performance, and they helped me to develop the solution for two other functions that suffer from chronic logistical problems; project management and distribution.* Our body of knowledge expanded by leaps and bounds. It became so broad and powerful that it deserved to be called a theory. We started to call it the Theory Of Constraints (TOC).

But that's not the end of the story. We didn't live happily ever after. A new devastating problem developed. Successful plants, plants having performance unmatched by anybody in industry, started to suffer a sudden deterioration, some even closed down.

I should have predicted it, but I didn't. Not until after the first few cases. In retrospect, it is so obvious. You improve production, and the constraint of the company moves outside production. What happens when it moves into an area where the constraint is not physical, but an erroneous policy? How do you then identify the constraint? How do you elevate it? How do you cause the needed changes in behavior? We didn't have any answers. And as a result....

The result is the throughput of the company stagnates. All the additional improvements in production do not lead to an increase in throughput but to an increase in excess manpower. And then it is just a matter of time until the market takes one of its downturns and the corporate tendency to cut costs kicks in. Where is the natural place to

---

* The five focusing steps also pointed to the possibility of a much better computer package for production—this time without using any sophisticated mathematical algorithm. Probably I felt the need to properly close this aspect of my work, because I invested considerable time and money to develop the logic and check the feasibility of such a computer system in a wide variety of plants. With THE HAYSTACK SYNDROME, published by North River Press, I put this section of the body of knowledge in the public domain. Determined not to allow the Institute to be bogged down in technical details, I dropped the software from the portfolio of the Institute.

look for cost reduction opportunities? In the places where there is apparent excess manpower–the areas that have improved the most. Punish people for their improvements and the process of ongoing improvement comes to a grinding halt. Morale, and thus performance, rapidly deteriorates. But at that time the clients have been spoiled by the excellent performance and they are not willing to accept any deterioration. Sales plummet, in some cases, to the extent that the financial viability is no longer there.

As a first reaction, we limited our business to plants where it was apparent that doubling the rate of production would still not cause the constraint to move into the market. Then the real work started.

It was apparent that everything that had been done until then was dealing with a specific case—the case where the constraint is physical. I needed to develop the generic thinking processes that would: 1. enable people to rapidly identify the core erroneous policy—the constraint; 2. enable construction of new policies that will not bring with them new devastating problems; and 3. enable construction of a feasible implementation plan that would not be hampered by resistance to change.

This swallowed most of our attention for five years. Once again I demanded we leave behind familiar and fertile territories and venture into unknown waters. Once again, I lost many excellent people (not as excellent as the ones who persevered). But this is a saga of its own.

What was needed now was to develop the generic procedures for using these thinking processes for the two common constraints - marketing and human relationships. I published the results of this work in my book, IT'S NOT LUCK.

Now that the danger of punishing people for doing what is right had been removed, the time had come to complete the work on production—to supply even better, effective tools to enable people to overcome the obstacles to implementation. This became more urgent then ever since the effectiveness of the solutions for marketing created situations where production had to jump their performance not in six months or three but in one.

I re-examined the obstacles.

1. Lack of ability to propagate the message throughout the company.

We knew that a book was not effective enough; too often people do not like to read books. But they do like (or at least do not resist) seeing a good movie. To turn THE GOAL into a movie we joined forces with American Media Incorporated, one of the most reputable companies in the field of training videos. It was quite an undertaking. We spent a great deal of time polishing the script to make it true to the book. And the movie did come out true to the book. A mistake.

As I've already mentioned, when THE GOAL was written I was ignorant of the five focusing steps. As a result, in the book the actions to identify, exploit, subordinate and elevate are all mixed and therefore it's quite difficult to transfer the knowledge into workable procedures. Why not correct it in the movie? Wasn't it too late? We decided to bite the bullet. We rewrote the script, walking the fine line between keeping the spirit of the original work and clearly outlining the steps that Alex Rogo and his gang followed.

The result? Due to AMI's efforts the new movie is a touching, educational movie. The best combination. In my eyes, the movie THE GOAL; The How-to Version, is better than the book. Now, at last, there is the means to expose the message to everybody within less than an hour. Obstacle # 1 is overcome.... But maybe I'm too optimistic. Time will tell.

What about the next obstacle?
2. Lack of ability to translate what they have learned from the book into workable procedures for their plant.

This was relatively easy to overcome. I had an excellent starting point—our two-day production workshop–the workshop that is based on a computer game, and was tested on literally tens of thousands of people. I invested the time to turn this workshop into a self-learning kit. Going through the self-learning kit, Drum-Buffer-Rope and Buffer-Management become intuitive. Moreover, I think a person who goes through it rigorously will be in a position to use it to teach others who do not have the stamina to work it out by themselves. This is an excellent springboard for plant personnel to construct the detailed, logistical procedures for their specific situation.

Obstacle #3: Lack of ability to persuade decision makers to allow the change of some of the measurements.

With the years, this obstacle has been severely eroded. TQM and JIT have done a lot to change upper management's outlook. The movie will also help. But the ultimate weapon was supplied by an unexpected ally. The Institute of Management Accountants sponsored a survey on actual implementations of TOC in industry. The 200-page report was published in 1995. Here is a quote from their conclusions:

> "The accounting in TOC should be familiar territory to management accountants. While the terms used in TOC are different from those we commonly use, variable costing, use of scarce resources, and responsibility accounting have been topics in management accounting textbooks for decades. From a theoretical viewpoint, little in TOC is new to accounting. The difference is that some topics—particularly, use of scarce resources—are far more important than we thought and are given more prominence in TOC. The companies involved in TOC are different from most companies in that they actually put into practice much of the advice found in the textbooks. Surveys over the last several decades have revealed consistently that most companies do not follow many of the practices advocated in management accounting textbooks. Absorption costing routinely is used for internal decision making, corporate headquarters expenses are allocated to divisions in performance reports, product profitability calculations ignore constraints, and so forth. For those of us who teach management accounting, it is reassuring that an identifiable collection of companies practice what we preach.

"What does the future hold for TOC? The most obvious applications are found in job shops, and managers of such shops will undoubtedly continue to mimic Alex Rogo's actions in *The Goal*. These efforts usually will be rewarded with almost immediate improvements in operations and in profits at virtually no cost. However, such efforts ultimately will lead to failure unless management outside of manufacturing is willing to embrace TOC or to evaluate manufacturing performance using TOC measures.

"Looking beyond the elements of TOC found in *The Goal*, our crystal ball becomes murkier. The Thinking Processes may be the most important intellectual achievement since the invention of calculus."

In the past fifteen years I've seen hundreds of implementations. I've heard of many more. They all seemed to be unique, yet they shared more than one common thread. I'm not talking just about the results: "These efforts usually will be rewarded with almost immediate improvements in operations and in profits at virtually no cost," or the actions: Identify, Exploit, Subordinate, etc. I'm talking about the common threads in the dynamics of the group.

I think that everybody would agree that the biggest obstacle to successful implementation is to overcome the resistance to change. The key is in knowing how to steer the dynamic of the interaction between people with different agendas and different levels of understanding.

Is there a generic way to do it? A proven path to reach a true consensus on the required change and on the actions to accomplish the change?

The common threads between the successful implementations caused me to suspect that there is a way. I started by looking for a specific dynamic in the resistance to change—looking to see if the type of reservations a person raises changes as his resistance erodes. It wasn't too difficult, I've had ample experience dealing with resistance to change (not always good experience—my numerous scars attest to that).

The first layer of resistance: raising problems having one thing in common—its out of our hands: vendors do not always deliver, clients change their mind at the last minute, workers are not properly trained, corporate forces on us....

[As long as this layer is not removed you are talking to the wall.]

The second layer of resistance: arguing that the proposed solution cannot possibly yield the desired outcome.

[Your proposed solution looks obvious to you, yet it doesn't to others. When you succeed to peel this layer, the real frustration starts. You clash smack into the next one.]

The third layer of resistance: "Yes, but..." Arguing that the proposed solution will lead to negative effects.

[You must have a lot of stamina and patience to fight this one. Or you're lucky to be born with tons of charisma. But when you pass it you haven't yet won the war.]

The forth layer of resistance: raising obstacles that will prevent the implementation.

[Succeed to remove this layer and the person is now on your side, but...]

The fifth layer of resistance: raising doubts about the collaboration of others (or worse, not raising their doubts).

No, it's not easy to overcome resistance to change. But, it's possible. Peeling, in sequence, all these layers turns resistance to change into the enthusiasm of an inventor.

Where do I stand in my research in production? Quite a while ago (1986-87) I found exactly how to move a person through the first two layers. I used this know-how in constructing the self-learning kit. It is possible now to peel the first two layers without the mandatory need for a knowledgeable instructor. As for the latter three layers, the situation might not be as satisfactory, it depends on the magnitude of the resistance. I hope that in most cases, the know-how contained in the self-learning kit will be enough.

For the tough cases I found a generic method that, in our experience, always works, but its translation to a specific plant requires a thorough knowledge of how to properly use the negative branches, the prerequisite tree and the transition tree of the thinking processes. Knowledge that I don't yet know how to satisfactorily teach through books. At least there are more and more people who have learned how to do it.

Overcoming resistance to change is still time consuming. Under ideal circumstances (all the relevant people are gathered in one room) it takes about five days. More research is needed, but for production, at last, there is a proven way to accomplish the mental change in one week and realize results in one month.

With the obstacles removed I do hope that we'll witness a sharp jump in plants' performance. Production is the heart of industry. Industry is the heart of a nation's wealth. When I retire, I would like to think that I've contributed something to strengthening it.

WHAT SHOULD YOU EXPECT?

Let me first tell you what I expect. I expect results.

Many text-books assume that in order to achieve results two things are needed:

> 1. Knowledge of what to change; the managerial know-how.
> 2. Knowledge of what to change to; the logistical know-how.

That's probably why they concentrate only on these two issues.

But as you suspect, these are not enough. Not even nearly enough. There is a third element that without it your efforts will not lead to results, they will lead only to higher levels of frustration.

Being a manager, frustration is not a foreign feeling for you. When are we frustrated? When we are under pressure from all sides, everybody is on our back, we are constantly fighting fires... and we don't know what to do.

There is a much higher level of frustration.   When we are under pressure from all sides, everybody is on our back, we are constantly fighting fires... and we know exactly what to do. But the [.....] don't want to listen!

You don't want to be in such a situation, and I don't want to bring you there. That's why, throughout this book, blended into the managerial and logistical know-how, you will also find:

> 3. Knowledge of how to cause the change; the psychological know-how.

No. This is not a book about the psychology of change. This is a book about how to jump the performance in production. That is the reason why it is composed the way it is:

Part one: In depth understanding of the problem.

Building the intuition for

Part two: Deriving the detailed solution.

This book is not what I call an easy book, but I think you'll find it stimulating and enjoyable. Learn, teach and harvest the results.

THE CORE PROBLEM
PART ONE

1 WHERE TO START?

Some of my friends suggested I start with a concise description of the TOC way to manage an organization. Others argued that, since this is a tutor guide for production, I should be more focused; I should start with a concise description of TOC for production–the drum-buffer-rope and the buffer-management methods.

Still others claimed that before that, I should state the objective – the type of expected results. They even suggested that I should start with some case studies. "Go right to the heart of the matter," they argued. "Show the readers how others rapidly jumped the performance of their operations. Tell them the real meaning of the words 'rapidly' and 'jump'. Describe cases where within just a few weeks companies increased the output of their operation by double digit percentages and did so without adding more people or more equipment."

I was not convinced. On the contrary, I think that this is a perfect example of how not to start. Does it build conviction? No. It builds skepticism. Just imagine the reaction of your peers and your people to the above statements. Such a beginning will cause us to clash into the first layer of resistance.

There is one prudent way to start. By listening. Let me prove it:

"The first layer of resistance: raising problems having one thing in common: 'Its out of our hands....' As long as this layer is not removed you are talking to the wall."

Anyone who ever tried to introduce a major change (and that is exactly what you'll do when you come to implement the know-how detailed in this book) is keenly aware of this layer of resistance. You clash into it when you praise a revolutionary suggestion, or even try to explain it. You try to show how we can improve and they tell you that it will never work. That you are missing the mark. That the problem is... and as long as... we cannot do a thing. They try to convince you that the problem actually is out of their hands. You try to address one of their concerns and they immediately raise another.

In your ears it starts to sound like they are going out of their way to block any real improvement. It sounds like they are raising excuses, pitiful excuses, just so that nothing will change.

As a result, you start to develop a not-too-complimentary opinion about them. They are resisting change. They are conservative and stubborn. As (if) you keep on pushing for your idea and they keep resisting, the superlatives become more and more unflattering. It won't be long before your opinion about their attitude will start to show in your arguments, or at least in your tone of voice and body language. People are sensitive to undertones and react to them. Keep on pushing and they will begin to view you as a fanatic; if you are in a position of power, as a dangerous fanatic.

You are blocked. I went to all this length to show what happens when you present people with a revolutionary suggestion.

Of course, one might argue that such a reaction will come only from certain groups, and that his/her people are much more open.

18

They might be very open but their reaction, I'm afraid, will be roughly the same. Expecting that a revolutionary suggestion (good as it is) will be greeted with open arms, is an illusion–a dangerous illusion. What is the reason? Bear with me while I explain.

Suppose that the people you have to convince in your organization are all open to change, all eager to improve. And on top of it, they have the brain-power and the experience needed to critically evaluate good suggestions and find the way to put them to work. What would be the reaction of such an open-minded group to your suggestion? Don't be too hasty to jump to a conclusion.

People who are eager to improve are not sitting on their hands waiting for you to suggest an improvement. They were and are trying to improve, and they have their conclusions about what is currently blocking further major improvements. Having brain-power and being experienced, it stands to reason that their conclusions are founded on hard facts.

Now suppose we are dealing with a situation where performance has stagnated, or is improving at a slow rate. Such a situation is a clear indication that these capable and eager-to-improve people have reached the stage where they believe that what currently impedes further major improvements is not under their direct control.

What happens when you approach such a group with a new suggestion? A suggestion that you claim will jump performance? Their natural, and logical, reaction is to expose you to their conclusions about the situation, to prove to you why it's out of their hands.

Try to ignore their conclusions, or even worse, try to brush them aside as excuses, and what do you expect their reaction will be?

Still, why don't they address your suggestion on its own merit? That's human nature:

A person having concrete opinions about what should be done is not open to others' suggestions.

If our suggestion has merit, if they can improve by addressing things which are under their control, it must be that there is a mistake in their conclusions. We should bring them to find it. How?

There is only one way. We must first listen to their arguments. But what does it mean to listen to their arguments?

Let's see.

2 WHY IS IT DIFFICULT TO MANAGE PRODUCTION - THE COMMON VIEW.

Why is it difficult to manage production?

1. _____
   _____

2. _____
   _____

3. _____
   _____

4. _____
   _____

5. _____
   _____

6. _____
   _____

7. _____
   _____

8. _____
   _____

Take your time answering the question, "Why is it difficult to manage production?" Don't just write the reasons you believe in, include what you think the others believe in; the superintendents, foremen, material managers, etc. Do it in writing because we'll refer to your list at later stages.

When you finish this tutor guide and you want to teach a group, ask each participant to compose their own list in his/her Work Book (see appendix, page 4). Then use a transparency of the above on an overhead projector to create the list of the group. Make sure that many are contributing to the list. Accept any suggestion and don't allow people to argue/discredit each other suggestions. Be firm about it otherwise it may turn into a finger pointing session.

3 RETHINKING THE COMMON VIEW.

As we said, to cause others to seriously entertain your suggestion you must first cause them to stop believing in their conclusions. How?

Look again at the list. Each item can be backed-up with ample examples from reality. There is no point in trying to persuade them that their speculated causes do not exist. They do.

We'll have to attack it in a different way. These people do want to improve; just notice the passion and anger in their voices when they complain about the reasons that make managing production so difficult. We should capitalize on their desire to have a more manageable operation.

Right now they regard the items on the list as key for improvement– improve on these items and we improve production. They are convinced that they know what should be done. We should bring them to realize that trying to eliminate this list does not really represent a solution, not if we call a solution something feasible that in the short term will significantly improve performance. If we succeed to convince them, their desire to improve will cause them to stop being enchanted by their conclusions.

No, it's not a major task, it's easy. For each item on your list, for each suggested reason, estimate three things: the feasibility of overcoming it, the cost involved and the time required.

	Feasibility	Cost	Time
1			
2			
3			
4			
5			
6			
7			
8			

For example: suppose that one item is "Workers are not trained well enough." Estimate the feasibility to train them well. Use terms like 'high' or 'low'. Now estimate the cost. Don't make a doctoral thesis out of it; throw out a number that looks reasonable. And then the estimated time; six months, two years, depending on your situation.

If you listed a reason like 'clients change their minds at the last minute' and you estimate the feasibility to rectify it as 'not a chance', then don't bother to estimate cost and time.

Do it for each item on your list. Take your time.

When you guide a group, don't ask every one to do it separately, rather use the transparency (page 5 of the workbook) to write the group estimations. Be careful to cut-off long arguments by choosing the estimation that is the most optimistic, and stress it. You want to make sure that every body will regard the results as tilted toward the more optimistic view. Don't spend more than twenty minutes on it, because the 'go-getters' among the group get irritated, and become more irritated with every five minutes that pass. When they finish, summarize with the conclusion drawn in the next paragraph.

Now that you have finished writing the evaluations for each item, review the emerging picture. What is the feasibility? What is the total cost? How much time will it take? Not too encouraging, is it?

No wonder the impression is that there is no quick fix, that it's simply not feasible to jump performance in the very near term. This is actually the case, unless....

Unless this list does not contain the major causes that make production so difficult to manage. If the major causes are missing and they are easy to fix, then it is possible to jump performance.

The problem is that people are convinced that their list is comprehensive, or at least, that it contains all the major causes. How can we bring them to realize that this is not the case?

Raising another speculated cause will not do. Judging by their reaction to each other's suggestions, we must expect that they will not accept our speculated cause as much more important than the ones they have already raised. We'll have to approach it in a different way.

What is the meaning of their claim that their list contains the major causes for the difficulty to manage production? It means that they claim that if this list of causes will be properly addressed then the result will be that production is relatively easy to manage.

THEY CLAIM THAT
IF: clients never change their mind
         and vendors always supply whatever we ask for, on time,
         and there are no absenteeism problems with the work-force
         and people are excellently trained and disciplined
         and all processes are reliable
         and machines never break down
         and quality is superb
         and data is readily available and accurate
         and **they can decide on whatever policies they want**,

THEN: managing production will be a piece of cake.

Is it really the case? It seems that there is no feasible way to check it. Where are we going to get such a paradise operation? Not in the real world.

We can't find it in the real world, but we can find it in the unreal world - a computer simulation.

When guiding a group use page 6 of the Work Book to make our claim. But, please, explain the logic we are using. The logic that if we want to check a claim that A is the major cause for B, then we can examine what will happen if A is eliminated. If the claim is right it must be that in the case that A is eliminated B will be significantly reduced in magnitude. If it doesn't happen and B is almost as large as before then the unavoidable conclusion is that A is not a major cause for B.

Make sure that everybody agrees with the logic before you proceed to the simulator.

4 THE SIMULATOR

As you are going to reveal, the simulator is essential in internalizing this know-how. Not only does it aid in recognition of the core problem, it is instrumental in digesting the solution. Moreover, without the simulator it is very difficult to peel away the first two layers of resistance.

At the same time, the simulator is an addictive game. The problem is that if people play the simulator without proper guidance, they may enjoy a good game but for them the simulator can no longer be used to teach them how to improve a real plant.

That is the reason I think that it is important that the simulator will be only in the hands of people who are studying this book (you) or people who are taught by people who had studied this book (people you may elect to teach). So please, don't lend the simulator without lending with it the book.

THANK YOU FOR YOUR COLLABORATION

First, you have to install the simulator on the hard disk of your computer. Put the CD in your drive and follow the installation instructions that appear on the CD.

Activate the simulator by double-clicking on the icon: GSim. A regular 'Open Window', common to so many Windows applications appears. It shows several files. All of them have the format of 'params.nnn', where nnn is a three digit number. Double click on 'params.310'.

The simulated environment appears on the screen.

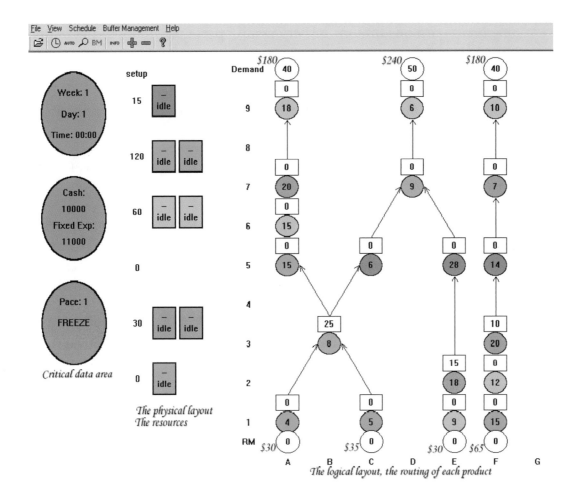

The physical layout
The resources

Critical data area

The logical layout, the routing of each product

What appeared are the two complementary representations of an operation. Yes, even a simple operation is not simple. Let's decipher what you see. On the left side you have some critical data items presented within three ellipses. Just to the right of the critical data area the physical layout where each colored box represents a resource is displayed. These resources can be machines or workers in a production plant, they can be physicians or nurses or an X-ray machine in a hospital, they can be clerks or committees in a service organization etc. We'll refer to them as resources.

The different resources have different capabilities. You have, under your control, one Blue resource (the top one), two identical green resources, two identical cyan resources, two identical magenta resources, and one brown. A very small operation. It shouldn't be too difficult to manage.

There are numbers written to the left of the resources. These numbers represent (in minutes) the time it takes a resource to prepare itself whenever it's assigned to a new task (set-up). For example the set-up time of the blue resource is 15 minutes, for a green resource it takes two hours, while the brown resource doesn't take any time to set-up to do a new task.

Now what are these resources supposed to do? The details of their tasks are described on the right part of the screen. Toward the bottom there is a row of letters A B C D E and F. These letters represent the code names of the parts (or missions) appearing in the columns above them.

Right above the letter F there is a white circle. It represents the raw-material needed in order to produce part F. In a hospital we don't call it raw-material but patient(s), in a bank it's paperwork, in an insurance agency we call it a prospect. Different organizations have different vocabularies but the concept is the same; we have to manage resources performing tasks.

Right now there is no raw-material F in the plant. Click on the seventh icon from the left, just below the menu. The purchase price of the each material now appears. Each unit of raw-material F will cost you $65. For your convenience we have included the purchase prices and the end product prices in their respective circles, but note that in the simulator you'll have to click on the 'Info' icon to get them. Now, click on the 'Info' icon again to get rid of the extra information and bring back the usual information you need at all times.

How do you purchase raw-material? You don't need to start the simulation run for that. All you have to do is to click on the circle that represents the raw-material you want to purchase. A window will be opened:

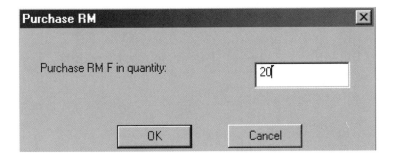

Put the appropriate quantity, say 20 units, and click on the OK button. In the simulator your suppliers are extremely responsive, they deliver immediately. At the same time you get the materials your suppliers are being paid. While the 20 pieces appear at the F Circle your cash is down. On the central ellipse on the left side, you can see how much cash you have, $8,700. At the start you had $10,000. You just paid 65 dollars for each of the twenty units you've purchased. You see, the simulator doesn't think for you, it doesn't make any decisions, it only executes your decisions, and updates the numbers accordingly.

Note that the time did not start to move. In the upper gray ellipse on the left side it is still week 1, day 1, and the time is 00:00. The red ellipse says it clearly: Freeze. That means you can take your time to purchase materials, plan and think. You can even allocate your resources to the operations steps while the simulation is in freeze mode.

Now that you have material F, you would probably like to do something with it; turn it into a sold good. For that you have to process it, to perform on it, in sequence, a set of tasks. Who is the resource that can perform the first task on raw-material F? Yes, it's the green resource. Notice, the green circle appearing above the letter F does not represent a resource, it just indicates which resource has to do the task. The number written in the green box tells the time in minutes it will take, on average, for a green resource to complete this task for each unit. In our case it will take 15 minutes per unit.

How do we activate a resource on a specific task? The resources are on the left side on the screen. In the middle of the screen there is a column of numbers from 1 (toward the bottom) to 9 (near the top). These numbers will help us in naming the various tasks. For example

the task that we now want the green resource to perform will be called
F1. Click on one of the green resources and drag it onto the green
circle in row 1 above the letter F; task F1. Then release the mouse. The
green circle at F1 now shows: +15. The green resource you've
allocated to the F1 production-step now shows:

 That means the particular unit of the green resources is now
assigned to stage F1 and it is in setup mode.

It is time to let the simulation start to run and time to proceed.
Click on the red ellipse, the one showing the word Freeze. Once you
do it, the color of the ellipse changes to green. Instead of 'Freeze' it
now shows 'Running'.

The clock starts to move. Watch the clock and notice that time flies on
the simulator. The simulator is now on it's slowest pace, pace 1, as
indicated the clock. You can increase and decrease the pace by clicking
on the icons "+" or "-" respectively, which are located at the left top of
the screen. You can also use the standard +and – keys. Note that pace
2 is twice as fast as pace 1, I would not recommend you do it now.

The clock is ticking but don't worry, you are not wasting time. Once
you are familiar with all commands you'll start again and then you'll
have to race against time.

According to the number on the left of the green resource a setup
should take, about, 120 minutes (not 120 minutes real-time, but 120
minutes of the simulator's clock time, where a whole week takes about
1 real-time hour).

Let's wait until these two simulated hours have passed. The mode of
the green resource has changed from setup to Prod, which means, "I'm
now Producing." When the resource starts processing both the
resource box and the task circle change to a net of green lines. Every
15 simulated minutes (on average) one unit is completed processing by
the green resource. Unit by unit the raw-material is moving from the
white circle with the raw materials to the green F1 circle for processing,
and then to the next white rectangle (where inventory are stored)

above it. As long as task F1 is displays with a net of green lines, meaning it is in the midst of processing, the sum of the units below and the units above is only 19 since one unit is being processed by the resource.

When all 20 pieces have been processed the green resource will enter the 'Idle' mode. The code F1 still appears on the resource (and the + sign still appears on F1 circle) indicating that the resource it still setup to do this job. So if you purchase more of raw-material F (which I don't recommend that you do now) the green resource is going to start producing right away without spending another two hours setting-up.

Another thing that you should be aware of is that you don't have to wait until all 20 units are processed at F1 before you can perform the next task. You know how to do it. What color is F2? So, click on one of the cyan resources (there are two), drag it onto the F2 Circle and release the mouse.

To continue processing this material through the remaining tasks you don't have to wait until the cyan resource starts to provide units, you can start setting-up a magenta resource for task F3. Do it now.

Since the processing time on F3 is relatively long - 20 minutes - you might elect to assign the second magenta resource to the same task. Yes, it is legitimate, why not? In almost all plants it's very common to see two resources performing the same task at the same time.

The screen is now a little bit less puzzling. The numbers in the colored circles represent the time in minutes it takes to process one unit and the numbers in the white boxes represent inventory.

You have probably noticed that right from the start of the simulation there was the number 10 written in the white rectangle above task F3. Now you know what it represents–work in process inventory. The plant wasn't empty to start with. There are more places with work in process. Even without purchasing any raw materials we could have activated the blue resource on F5, or on E5, or on C5. We couldn't perform all three tasks simultaneously because we have only one blue resource, so we have to choose. Since we have already started to process F, why won't we continue. Activate the relevant resources on task F5, on task F7 and on task F9. *

Above task F9 there is a white circle that contains the number 40. This is the market demand, this week, for product F. Watch how the number 40 goes down as units are processed through task F9, and watch how your cash register registers accordingly (the selling price for the F product is $180 dollars a unit).

When day 1 finishes the clock freezes and you get a message that marks the end of the day, with data concerning the throughput and inventory-dollar-days at the end of the day. We'll explain those numbers later. Click on the OK button to get rid of the message. You are still in a freeze mode. Click on the Freeze ellipse when you are ready to continue.

Okay. Producing one product is not enough. You have two other products D and A that you are committed to deliver this week. They are done by the same resources, but don't worry, before we committed on the quantities to be delivered (40 units of A, 50 units of D and 40 units of F) we made sure that you have the available capacity on each and every resource type to do the job (of course if you do not waste it). You know how to purchase raw-materials, you know how to activate each resource on each one of its tasks. You might need some further explanations on tasks B3 and D7.

Look first at task D7. It's an assembly operation. To process one unit at D7, it needs one unit coming from E5 and one unit coming from C5. There is no point in asking the brown resource to work at task D7 if inventory is not available from one of the relevant feeding tasks.

B3 is also assembly operation. It needs units from tasks A1 and C1. But the units that it produces (there were 25 of these units already completed to start with) are needed both for product A and product D. If you activate the blue resource on task C5 the units will go to the

---

[1] If you ask a resource to perform a task which it is not supposed to do (like when you are drag the blue resource to task F7 which is supposed to be done by the purple) the simulator doesn't accept it.

right (to product D). If instead you activate the green resource on task A5 the units will go to the left (to product A). If you want only a limited number of units to go one way, you can give the corresponding resource the appropriate instruction. Let see how to do it.

Assign a green resource to perform task A5. Now click on the A5 circle. You get the following window:

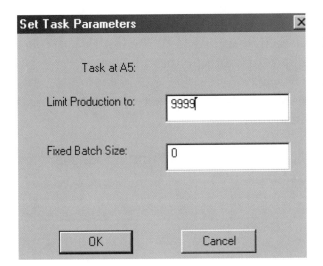

The production-step is set to a very high number, 99999. You surely wish to limit it to a much smaller number. Type the number 10, for example, and then click on the OK button to confirm. You can always click on any task circle and see what its current limit is.

If you wish you can always click on the 'Info' icon at the top and see the limit on every task that is limited.

When the Green resource will finish processing the 10 units you allowed him to process, it will stop processing and be idle. But on the resource box the mode would be 'Hold' indicating that it's not lack of materials but your instruction that caused it to stop processing.

You don't have to wait any longer. Run with it, purchase material, assign resources, deliver what we have committed to, until the simulated week is over (five days, 8 hours a day). When the week is over, a screen showing your results will appear. It details your financial results, your production results and your marketing results. Of course you haven't scored high. Half the week was wasted learning how to activate the simulator. So we'll start again, from the beginning. But first let's have a small chat.

To purchase: Click on the raw material circle, fill in the quantity and confirm by clicking on OK. Click on the Freeze ellipse to continue the run.

To assign a resource to a task: Click on the resource unit box and drag the mouse to the appropriate task, then release the mouse.

To limit a task: click on the task circle and type in the limit. Then click on OK. Click on the Freeze ellipse to continue the run.

To get information on time remaining for set-up and quantity remaining on limit: Click on the 'Info' icon.

To freeze the simulator: Click on the Freeze/Running ellipse – the bottom ellipse on the left side of the screen.

When guiding a group, use a data projector to project the simulator on a large screen to explain how to run it. Follow the explanation step-by-step, making sure that everyone is with you at each step. When you finish give them about 15-25 minutes to practice the mechanics of running the simulator. Encourage each one, individually, to start producing the other products. Watch how each one is doing it. It will give you the opportunity to identify and go over the details that they didn't fully grasp.

5 MANAGING A "PARADISE ENVIRONMENT"

Before you start the simulator again, let's remind ourselves of our purpose for doing it (besides having fun).

We started with the question: why is it so difficult to manage production? You constructed a list of answers that represents the opinions of the managers in your company. When you estimated the feasibility, cost and time required to deal properly with that list, the emerging picture was not too encouraging. The list contained too many discouraging causes; (a discouraging cause: a cause that has low feasibility to be rectified or requires heavy investments and a lot of time). It seems as if there is no quick fix. It seems that it will take a lot of effort and time to gradually improve production's performance.

Only one hope remains to rapidly jump performance, the hope is that all the discouraging causes are <u>not</u> the major causes that makes managing production so difficult. If that's the case, something else must be the main cause – the core problem - and maybe it won't be so difficult to fix! To test this long shot we are using the simulator.

The simulator presents a relatively simple operation – considerably less resources and products than what you have to manage in your real operation. The visibility that you have on the simulator is by far better then what you can hope for in your real plant – all of the information is displayed on one screen, real-time and it's accurate.

On top of it, everything is already in top shape: all of the resources are well trained and disciplined, quality is perfect, each individual process is under control, machines never break down. Even the outside world is perfect: vendors are extremely reliable and responsive, clients never change their minds. But above all, you are free to set your policies in any way that you like.

It should be easy to manage the simulated "Paradise Plant." Or, more accurately, it should be if the reasons that were listed (and which are non-existent in Paradise) are actually the major reasons which make managing production such a difficult task.

You are going to test it. Numerically. The prices of the orders that you have to fulfill this week (you have enough capacity to fulfill them all) guarantee that the plant will be very profitable. After paying expenses at the end of the week ($11,000) you should make $5450 net profit; if you deliver on your commitment to your clients, that is.

Not delivering on your commitments, your firm orders, is bad, but we'll be generous. Allowing for glitches we'll accept a net profit as low as $4500, but less than that....

You have only one run. The reason for limiting you to one run is that if you run over and over again, the result will be that you'll eventually develop the intuition to score high on the simulated plant but you'll never learn how to score high in your real plant. At this stage the simulator is an essential teaching aid, not a matching game.

If you don't yet feel comfortable with the simulator commands, you are allowed to do one more trial run. Click on the Open icon (the leftmost icon just below the File menu) and call PARAMS.310 again.

At this stage you know how to handle the simulator. If you still feel insecure it's not because of the simulator, it's your intuition trying to tell you what the real cause is that makes managing production such a challenging task.

Now, take your time, as long as you want, to plan exactly how you are going to run the simulated plant. When you are ready, start again. You have one real-world hour to complete the week. So, if you are holding the simulator on "freeze" for too long, we trust you to increase the pace of the simulator's clock (only go up to pace 5).

Plan carefully and then execute well. Please register your results. I would wish you good luck, if luck had anything to do with the results. Go.

Run Result

Financial Results

Net profit _____

Cash _____

Return on investment _____

Throughput _____

Inventory _____

Operating expenses _____

Utilization of resources

Resource	% production	% set up
Blue	_____	_____
Green	_____	_____
Cyan	_____	_____
Magenta	_____	_____
Brown	_____	_____

Order Fulfillment

Product	Quantity required	Quantity delivered
A	_____	_____
D	_____	_____
F	_____	_____

When guiding a group review the purpose of running the simulator, then allow them a maximum of 20 minutes for planning and 45 minutes for the actual run. Before they start planning warn them that you will be using the pace option to guarantee that everyone finishes within the allotted time.

To prevent pitiful excuses from being given as the reasons for unsatisfactory results, make sure to approach each one about the time that s/he reaches day four, and jokingly ask if s/he has the feeling of running the plant by the seat of his/her pants. The response is usually embarrassed agreement.

Guide them to record their results in their individual books but don't write their results on the board, and don't allow the higher scorers to brag. Make sure that they understand that a result lower than $4500 is not a reason to brag.

6 WHAT MIGHT THE CORE PROBLEM BE?

Well, how did you do?

No. Don't try it again. List the undesirable effects you witnessed while running the simulated plant.

1.	
2.	
3.	

If you are not a startling exception you probably haven't succeeded to ship all the orders the plant committed to deliver to its clients. And it wasn't because of lack of capacity. Yes, you would like to have some more resources; at the beginning of the week you wished that you had more green resources, at the end more cyan's and throughout more blue. But the fact is that a lot of time was wasted during the week, as can be seen by the percent utilization of the resources. Probably none of them were utilized to even the 95% level.

And what about your planning? If you are like most experienced people, your meticulous planning was not carried out beyond day two or three. You had to deviate from it because of one reason or another.

You probably drifted to the most popular method – run the plant by watching what should be done now; this resource is idle, that one doesn't have material, here is material being neglected, that resource is over producing. Almost like in a real plant, where fires and expediting are part of the norm.

Even in "Paradise Plant" it is difficult to manage production. Moreover it's not just difficult but all the bad effects are still here, in all their might!

1. Not all customers' orders are shipped on time.

2. Original plans have a limited life.

3. There are a lot of course corrections (expediting).

Examine now your original list and erase from it any listed item that does not exist in the simulator (those things can not be the major cause).

What is left?

We must go back to the original question: "What is the cause for all that?"

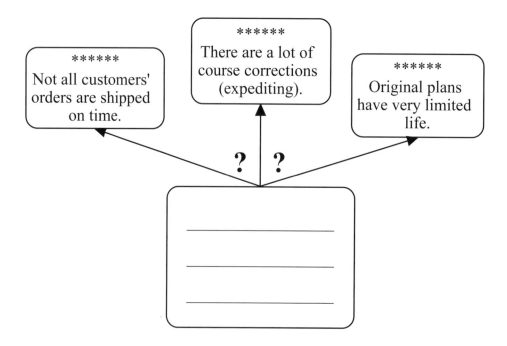

When guiding a group use the list of the above three undesirable effects, to conduct a group discussion. Get an agreement that the group performance on the "paradise plant" proves that the main cause that makes managing production so difficult is still unknown.

Then use the above chart to solicit answers. Down play excuses like, "we forgot..." or "I didn't pay attention to...". Don't write any suggested answer, not even when some bright and honest individuals will suggest that the real reason is that they (the collective they) don't really know how to run a plant. Don't write any answer because even if it is right, it's unlikely that people, at this stage, will truly agree with it.

We can get a clue to where the answer lies if we pay attention to how people are running the simulator. On the one hand, their decisions about which resource to activate where, are impacted by the desire to ship products and score a sale ("We have units after task F7. Where is the cyan resource so we can finish them up and ship them out?"). On the other hand, their decisions are impacted by the fear that if we don't utilize the resources now we will not have the needed capacity later ("The blue resource is idle, let's move it here. The cyan is idle now, let's move it there").

I think that this behavior is a reflection of the more general conflict facing management. To fully understand this conflict, view the "logical tree" on next page.

We can't be terribly wrong if we assume that the objective of most managers is to properly manage their area of responsibility (Statement # 10 on the tree). But what does it mean to manage properly? The two dominating principles that guide managers are that wasting cost is bad (statement # 15) and that throughput (sale) is essential for the survival (statement 20).

From that we can draw two unavoidable results:

1. If managers try to manage properly, and they are guided by the principle that wasting cost is bad, then we must find that managers try to control cost (statement 25).

2. If managers try to manage properly, and they are guided by the principle that throughput is essential, then we must find that managers try to protect throughput (statement 30).

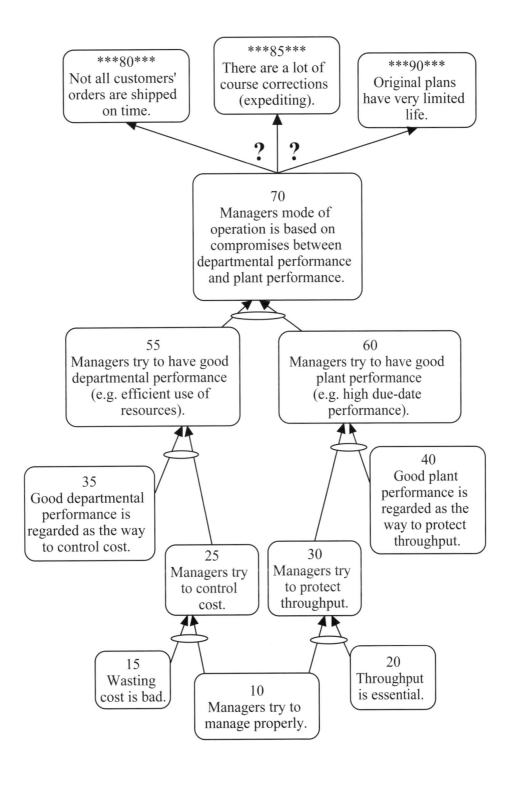

80
Not all customers' orders are shipped on time.

85
There are a lot of course corrections (expediting).

90
Original plans have very limited life.

? ?

70
Managers mode of operation is based on compromises between departmental performance and plant performance.

55
Managers try to have good departmental performance (e.g. efficient use of resources).

60
Managers try to have good plant performance (e.g. high due-date performance).

35
Good departmental performance is regarded as the way to control cost.

40
Good plant performance is regarded as the way to protect throughput.

25
Managers try to control cost.

30
Managers try to protect throughput.

15
Wasting cost is bad.

10
Managers try to manage properly.

20
Throughput is essential.

Do you agree with the logic? Do you agree that the two predicted results – that managers try to control cost and that they try to protect throughput – do exist in reality?

Let's bring two other common beliefs into the picture: Good department performance is regarded as the way to control cost (statement 35) and good plant performance is regarded as the way to protect throughput (statement 40).

What are now the unavoidable conclusions?

On one hand, if managers try to control cost, and good department performance is regarded as the way to control cost, then managers try to have good department performance. E.g. efficient use of resources - "The blue resource is idle let's move it here, the cyan is now idle let's move it there" (statement 55).

On the other hand, if managers try to protect throughput, and good plant performance is regarded as the way to protect throughput, then managers try to have good plant performance. E.g. high due-date performance - "We have units after stage F7. Where is the cyan resource so we can finish them and ship them out?" (statement 60).

Working on the simulator demonstrates how difficult it is to concentrate on two different things at the same time. In a real plant the desire to achieve both good department performance and good plant performance may turn into a tug-of-war.

Which is the function that is most concerned with shipping on time - with plant performance? The expediters. Which is the function that is concerned most with department performance? The foremen. What is usually the type of relationship between these two functions? A tug-of war. (The same conflict and thus the same situation exists in engineering between department heads and project managers).

And the unavoidable result: managers' mode of operation is based on compromises between the desire to have good department performance and the desire to have good plant performance (statement 70).

Can it be that these compromises are the cause for our difficulties in managing production? Can it be that these compromises are the cause for the undesirable effects?

Can it be that these compromises are the core problem?

When guiding a group use a slide of the logical tree. Read the "logical tree" out loud, as it was presented here. Start at the bottom, and get agreement on the entry statements. Then, using "If... and...Then..." continue reading slowly upwards. Get agreement from everyone on each conclusion as you read up the logical tree.

7 THE EFFICIENCY SYNDROME.

Let's examine a specific example of a compromise between the desire to have good departmental performance and good plant performance.

If managers try to have good department performance then one of the things that will be considered as bad is resources standing idle. As a matter of fact, in most organizations it looks like the motto is:
"IF A WORKER DOESN'T HAVE ANYTHING TO DO, LET'S FIND HIM SOMETHING TO DO!"

It's not only a policy, it's a behavior pattern.   And at all levels. Workers don't want to be caught standing idle, supervisors are looking for work for their people, managers strive to have high efficiency numbers, and most corporations will interfere if efficiencies are too low.

At the same time these organizations need to have good plant performance – they do have to supply on-time to their clients.

Is there a clash between high efficiencies and delivering on time? And if there is, what are the undesirable effects that will stem from the resulting compromises? We have an excellent opportunity to check it. You and the simulator.

We'll ask you to run the simulator again, but this time you will run the simulated operation under the efficiency behavior pattern.   The comparison between the last run and this run will give you first hand experience with the net impact of the "efficiency syndrome".

To simulate the eagerness of workers to be (or at least to look) busy you'll have to put the resources on "auto-activation". That function is invoked by clicking on the 'Auto' icon at the top of the screen just below the menus: AUTO . Once you have clicked on that icon you'll get:

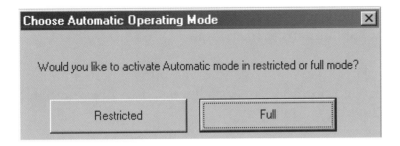

Click on the 'Full' button to ensure that all operations would be under the influence of the auto-activation mode.

Under the feature of 'Auto-activation' any idle resource would automatically assign itself to any task that has some material in front of it. It is allowed to take initiatives and activate itself. You will notice that the blue resource assigned itself to the biggest pile of work, on task E5. If you don't like it, you can give it another instruction and it will obey. For that you'll have to click on the blue resource box, drag it to another task, for instance F5, and release the button. The Blue resource will switch itself to work on task F5.

Some of the resources are now either idle or about to be idle. There is simply not enough material in the plant. You yourself, will have to behave according to the "efficiency syndrome," no matter how stupid it looks to you personally. Purchase additional raw-material so that the resources can achieve high efficiency numbers.

Remember, the percent utilization of each resource is recorded, and at the end of the week you'll be judged accordingly. So don't try to waste set-ups on the green resource, on the end of the week report, actual production is registered separately from set-up. To guarantee a high score on the percent utilization report, you'll have to purchase more of raw-material F and E. Don't worry, you will need this material to satisfy next week's orders.

You don't have to purchase it all at the beginning of the week, but when you see a resource or two standing idle you'd better purchase immediately. If at the end of the week the average utilization of all resources is not above 70 percent, you have cheated yourself. By the way, try to imagine what happens in a regular company, to a plant manager who, on average, registers less than 70% utilization of his/her work-force!? And what happens to his people?

So plan carefully because you still have to make money, you still have to deliver everything we promised to our clients. Run the simulator according to the following guidelines:

- "If a worker doesn't have something to do, let's find him something to do!"

- Workers don't want to be caught standing idle.

- Supervisors look for work for their people.

- Managers strive to have high efficiency numbers.

- Corporate will "interfere" if efficiencies are too low.

When you finish, fill in the following:

RUN RESULTS WITH
EFFICIENCY SYNDROME
Financial Results

Net profit	_____
Cash	_____
Return on investment	_____
Throughput	_____
Inventory	_____
Operating expenses	_____

Utilization of resources

Resource	% production	% set up
Blue	_____	_____
Green	_____	_____
Cyan	_____	_____

Magenta _____ _____
Brown _____ _____

Order Fulfillment

Product	Quantity required	Quantity delivered
A	_____	_____
D	_____	_____
F	_____	_____

When guiding a group use a slide with the above bullets. Take your time and steer the discussion toward the efficiency syndrome in your organization. Encourage the group to bring examples. Raise the question of what will be the response of the hourly people if, all of a sudden, a manager says that it's okay to stay idle. Speculate with the group what is the likely interpretation of the work force of such a statement. Make sure that the examples show that the efficiency syndrome exists at all levels. Then use the following bullets to explain the next run and allow a maximum of one hour for the run. Make sure that they record their run results.

Put all resources on 'Auto-activation' (the third icon from the left, just below the main menu.

Release enough material to keep everybody busy.

Continue releasing material to keep everybody busy.

Don't try to reach your efficiency targets by wasting too much time on set-ups. You'll be caught.

The green machines are very expensive. If efficiency is too low corporate (the facilitator) will come to "help" you.

Still meet your shipping and financial targets.

Now, that you finished the simulated 'efficiency' run, do you have a stronger feel for the conflict between good departmental performance and good plant performance? And this was just an example!

List the undesirable effects you noticed in this last run.

1.	
2.	
3.	
4.	

When everybody is finished, use such a slide as above to get from the group the resulting undesirable effects. For each effect write, in parenthesis, the average magnitude relative to the previous run. Encourage a discussion about why we have the efficiency syndrome and if it really makes sense to have it.

Then present the following tree. Read it using if...and... then... It will cement the discussion.

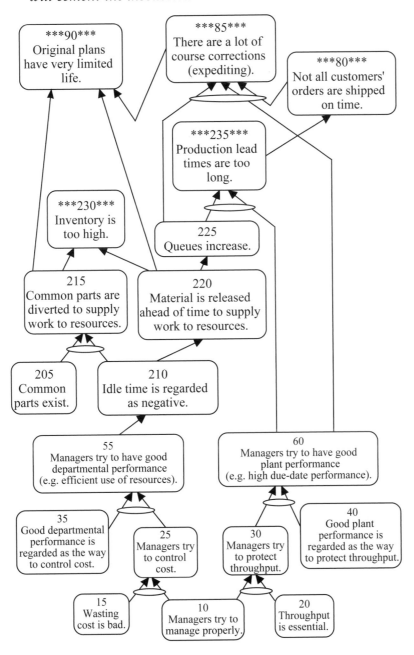

Let's analyze what happened.

As we already said, if managers try to have good departmental performance (statement 55) then the direct consequence is that idle time is regarded as negative (statement 210).

This being the case, managers must make sure that their workers do not stand idle. And if there is not enough work on the shop-floor, they make sure that there will be, even if it means releasing work now that was scheduled to be released later (statement 220).

But something else might happen as well. It might happen that the material that was released was intended for other products – another order (yes, in almost every plant there are common parts, common to more than one product - statement 205). The notion that staying idle is negative sometimes results in common parts being diverted just so that some resources will have something to do (statement 215). You probably almost blew your top when it happened on the simulator (at tasks A5 or C5) but that is exactly the reaction of a material manager when it happens in a real plant (and it does happen).

Releasing material ahead of time, for whatever reason, increases inventory (statement 230). In the case of common parts it causes another bad effect. This material was intended for another order, an order that now will be delayed (215 leading to statement 90).

What is the unavoidable result of releasing material ahead of time? Queues, in front of resources, increase (statement 225). Larger queues mean that on average material has to spend more time in the pipe, or in other words, it means that the production lead-time becomes longer. If the market demands fast reaction, as it does lately, then from the point of view of plant performance those long lead times might be considered as TOO long (235).

If production lead times are too long, it stands to reason that our sales people, in their eagerness to get the sale, promise to clients delivery times which do not have a lot of spare time relative to our average performance. And thus it's no wonder that not all customers' orders are shipped on time (80).

Delivering on time is essential for good plant performance. Any time managers realize that an order is late (or about to be late) they give it higher priority. These priorities do have an impact, they cause the relevant tasks to jump to the head of the queues. Of course, it doesn't happen by itself, in plants they call it "course corrections," or simply "expediting" (85).

You see how the desire to have good departmental performance clashes directly with the desire to have good plant performance. If we want to break this conflict we must first realize how deep it is.

8 THE "COST WORLD" AND THE "THROUGHPUT WORLD".

The gap between plant performance and departmental performance is so wide that there is not a satisfactory compromise (even theoretically). Let's prove it.

As we said the two dominating principles that guide managers decisions and actions are:

1. Save cost
2. Protect throughput.

What we have to realize is the extent these principles dictate contradicting modes of operation. For that it will behoove us to view the organization as a chain composed of many links. This is a natural analogy. In our organization, for example, one link is purchasing, another starts production, another finishes production, another assembles, another ships to the clients, another has to get the clients, yet another has to get the money from the clients, etc. Our organization is a chain composed of many links.

For a physical chain, what is the equivalent of cost?

We are paying for each and every link - cost is drained by every link. If we want to know the total cost we just have to add the cost of all the links. It is equivalent to the weight of the chain. Each link has a weight, and if we want to know the total weight of the chain, we just have to add up the weight of all the links.

Now, suppose you want to improve the chain - to save cost - to reduce its weight. And putting your mind to it, and time and money, you succeed to reduce the weight of one link by, let's say, one hundred grams. How much did you impact the weight of the entire chain? You reduced it by one hundred grams, no matter which link you improved. The local improvement translates, one to one, to be the improvement of the entire chain. As long as we are guided by the desire to reduce cost our understanding is that any improvement of any link is an improvement of the chain.

The resulting mode of operation is:

Good global results are equal to the sum of good local results.

This mode of operation we call the "cost world." The cost world naturally emphasizes departmental performance.

Now let's turn our attention to the other principle, that of protecting throughput. For a physical chain, what is the equivalent of throughput (sales)?

The throughput of an organization is not achieved by the efforts of just one link, but by the combined efforts of all. The throughput of the organization is not the throughput of one department PLUS the throughput of the next department. On the contrary, if just one department drops the ball, what happens to throughput?

Throughput is equivalent to the strength of the chain. The strength of the chain is not the strength one link PLUS the strength of the next link. If one link breaks, the chain breaks.

Now suppose you want to improve the chain - to improve throughput - to increase its strength. And putting your mind to it, and time and money, you succeed to increase the strength of one link by, let's say, a factor of three. By how much did you impact the strength of the entire chain?

Everybody knows that the strength of the chain is dictated by the strength of its weakest link. The vast majority of the links are not the weakest link. Improving the strength of any of those links doesn't contribute, even one iota, to the strength of the chain. As long as we are guided by the desire to gain throughput, our understanding is that most improvements of most links do not improve the chain.

The resulting mode of operation is:

Good global results are not equal to the sum of good local results.

This mode of operation we call the "throughput world". The throughput-world naturally ignores departmental performances as non-relevant, and concentrates solely on plant performance.

The cost world and the throughput-world modes of operation are in direct contradiction to each other. And when two modes of operation directly contradict, there is no satisfactory compromise.

In almost any operation we can see to what extent managers are not happy with their compromises. No, I'm not just talking about the relationships between a foreman and an expediter, I'm talking about the fact that managers are constantly changing the compromises.

Take, for example, the extreme case of "the end of the month phenomena," still prevailing in so many operations. In those organizations, at the beginning of the month, departmental performance is dominant: overtime is not easily approved, batch sizes are monitored to gain low variances. Toward the end of the month, all the rules change: they work weekends, they frantically expedite. At that time almost everything is allowed in the name of "Get the goods out the door!" Plant performance dominates.

To some extent, the same change in emphasis exists everywhere. Just notice the change in behavior in your operation when an important client order is about to be late.

We have lived with these compromises for so long, that we have almost gotten used to them. But in the last decade or so, our uneasiness has continued to grow. The competition in the market, that becomes fiercer and fiercer every year, leaves less and less slack for sloppy performance. If ten years ago we shipped 80% on time,

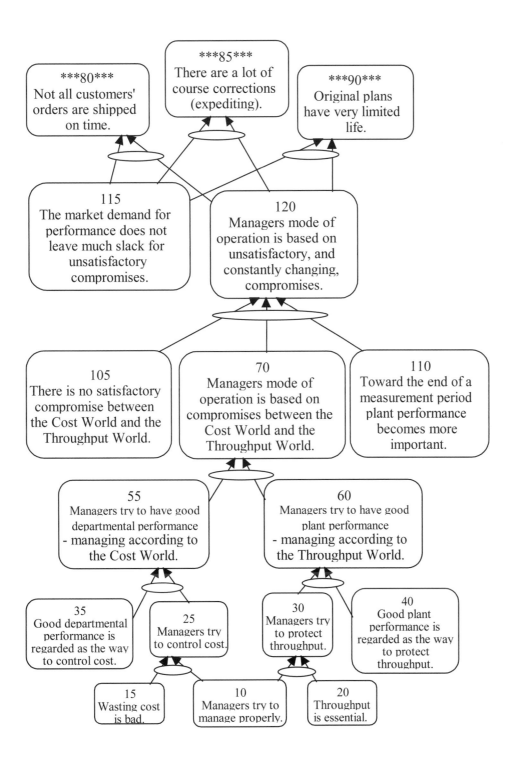

80
Not all customers' orders are shipped on time.

85
There are a lot of course corrections (expediting).

90
Original plans have very limited life.

115
The market demand for performance does not leave much slack for unsatisfactory compromises.

120
Managers mode of operation is based on unsatisfactory, and constantly changing, compromises.

105
There is no satisfactory compromise between the Cost World and the Throughput World.

70
Managers mode of operation is based on compromises between the Cost World and the Throughput World.

110
Toward the end of a measurement period plant performance becomes more important.

55
Managers try to have good departmental performance - managing according to the Cost World.

60
Managers try to have good plant performance - managing according to the Throughput World.

35
Good departmental performance is regarded as the way to control cost.

25
Managers try to control cost.

30
Managers try to protect throughput.

40
Good plant performance is regarded as the way to protect throughput.

15
Wasting cost is bad.

10
Managers try to manage properly.

20
Throughput is essential.

everything was fine, today we ship 95% on time and our ungrateful clients still bitch and moan. Compromises that we could live with ten years ago are not satisfactory any more.

View carefully the logical tree:
In statements 55 and 60 the terminology of "cost world" and "throughput world" are introduced. Therefore statement 70 becomes: managers' mode of operation is based on compromises between the "cost world" and the "throughput world".

Statement 105 brings forth our realization that there is no satisfactory compromise between these two modes of operation. Statement 110 brings forth our realization that our compromises are changing according to when the system as a whole is judged. This modifies the conclusion to be: managers' mode of operation is based on unsatisfactory, and constantly changing, compromises (120).

Add the realization of the market becoming more demanding (115) and you reach the explanation of why we suffer from the undesirable effects.

When guiding a group, use the following to explain the conceptual difference between the cost world and the throughput world:

COST WORLD

Chain analogy:

Prime measurement - WEIGHT
Any improvement of any link is an improvement of the chain.

GOOD GLOBAL RESULTS = SUM OF GOOD LOCAL RESULTS.

THROUGHPUT WORLD

Chain analogy:

Prime measurement - STRENGTH
Most improvements of most links do not improve the chain.

GOOD GLOBAL RESULTS • SUM OF GOOD LOCAL RESULTS.

Then go over the tree. Don't assume that it's too complicated or too "theoretical" for anybody. It isn't. Besides, the concepts of cost-world and throughput-world are essential in providing the members of the group with the terminology they need to reshape their intuition.

9 THE BATCH SIZE SYNDROME

So far we've seen only one tangible example of a cost-world dictate – the efficiency syndrome; a dictate that forces upon us unsatisfactory compromises. Using only one example is dangerous. It might blind us from seeing the broad spectrum of unsatisfactory compromises we impose upon ourselves; and as a result we might be tempted to deal only with the symptom–the efficiency syndrome, and not with the core problem – the clash between the cost-world and the throughput-world. At least one other example is necessary. Here it is:

"What do you mean spending two hours on a set-up and then producing for only half an hour?"

Where, do you think, such a reaction comes from?

From the cost-world, where the focus is on controlling costs. As long as this is the focus, saving cost-per-unit is a natural tendency; especially when managers are operating under the notion that the cost-per-unit impacts the sales price of the product, or at least its profitability.

Of course, this raises the question: For how long should we run the machine? Or, in other words, what should the batch size be? A lot is written about this subject, it's called economical batch quantity or economical order quantity. Almost nothing is written about the devastating impact of the compromises it forces on managers in operations. You are going to use the simulator to get a first hand impression of the impact. But first let's, briefly, review the cost world considerations.

Yes, we have to go through this if we want, not just to bitch and moan, but to arrive at concrete solutions of what to do about it. No matter which organization you are in, it suffers to some extent from this syndrome. Your organization might not use work-orders, like the defense contractors do, nevertheless, batching exists. Sometimes it's because of technical reasons, like curing ovens. Sometimes it's the marketing organization batching orders, sometimes it's a secretary batching her typing work, and always it's committees that batch work. One way or another you suffer from it, so you'd better go through this chapter.

Imagine that saving cost-per-unit is a desirable objective what should you consider? In order to save cost-per-unit, we must save set-up cost-per-unit. At the same time, in order to save cost-per-unit, we must also save carrying cost-per-unit. Two necessary conditions that have to be simultaneously satisfied. Here is a diagram that depicts that conflict:

BATCH SIZE DILEMMA IN THE COST WORLD

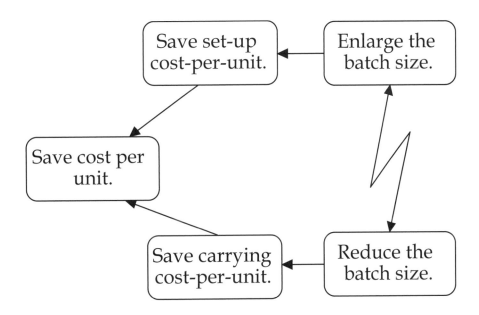

The problem is that, in order to save set-up cost-per-unit we must enlarge the batch size, while in order to save carrying cost-per-unit we must reduce the batch size. We have a conflict.

The cost-world compromise is to compute the total cost per unit (the set-up cost plus the carrying cost) and to look for the batch size that will result in the minimum cost. A typical compromise. In reality, where a batch has to go through several work centers, and the production lead times are not easily calculated, it's not as easy to calculate it as it is in the books. But we do the best we can to be in line with the above two necessary conditions. For example, in our simulated plant (where the weekly orders are around fifty units, each part goes through about six processing stages, the set-up times are on the order of magnitude of an hour and the run time per unit is on the order of magnitude of ten minutes) a batch size of twenty units will be considered as almost too small.

There is another aspect to the batch size – the control aspect, the paper work. In many operations (especially in the defense industry) each batch must carry with it the paper-work on which the actual process and set-up times are recorded. This is done to enable control, more accurate cost data, and trace-ability. As a result it is required that the integrity of the batch will be maintained; that batches will not be split on the shop floor.

On its own merit it might make sense, but does it make sense when we consider the throughput-world? When we consider that the operation must, at the same time, satisfy market demands?

Use the simulator to answer these questions. Return to the simulator but this time call for plant 312 (click on the Open icon, the leftmost icon, and double-click on PARAMS.312). It's exactly the same plant that you ran before, exactly the same except this time we have imposed the batch size syndrome. Once the screen is up, click on the 'Info' icon and see that on every operation it is written: B:20; it indicates the (relatively small) batch size that you have to work with. In a minute you'll see what a straight-jacket it is. There is one piece of good news. To get the sense of the net impact of the batch size syndrome we free you from the need to strive for high efficiencies.

Click again on the 'Info' icon to get the regular time-per-part numbers displayed. Now assign the blue resource to task C5 (click, drag and drop the blue resource to C5). Click on the freeze and let time pass until the setup finishes and processing starts. At that minute the inventory just above B3 goes down all the way from 25 to 5. Look at the blue resource itself. At the bottom of the resource we see the number 19. One piece is at the machine itself, while 19 are waiting for processing and cannot be used to anything else. As the blue resource continues to process, the batch is released, unit by unit, to the inventory bank above it.

Increase the pace to 2 by clicking on the '+' icon. Not before long, the blue resource finishes the twenty units. There are still 5 units available but the resource stops processing. Why? Because the resources were instructed to work only on whole batches of twenty. Of course, you as the manager in charge can, on a case-by-case basis, override it. Click on the C5 circle and then mark the box 'One-time override batch' and then click OK. The blue resource grabs whatever is available (5 units) and continues to process. Let it finish.

Now assign the blue resource to task E5. It sets itself up, but doesn't take the 15 units which are ready for it. There isn't a whole batch of 20 there to take. You can, once again, instruct the resource to disobey the plant policy of using only whole batches, but you also can complete the batch. Purchase 5 pieces of material E. Assign a cyan resource to task E1 then override the batch for E1. The cyan resource took the 5 available units and is now busy doing the set-up. Now assign a magenta resource to E2. You'll have to patiently wait until all 5 units will be processed by the cyan resource, and then come back to the magenta resource to override the batch for E2 as well. Only when the magenta resource finishes processing these five units can the Blue resource take the batch.

Realize that each time you override the batch policy you violate the cost-world policy in order to satisfy the throughput-world needs.

Run the simulator for two more days to get used to making these compromises. Now carefully plan the entire week because you still have to make money, you still have to deliver everything we promised to our clients.

1. Choose whether or not to put resources on Auto-activation. You may change this decision throughout the run.

2. Only you can decide to deviate from the instruction to always maintain the integrity of a work order, meaning use the override command, but DO NOT cancel the batch policy.

3. In your plant everyone is trying to maintain the integrity of the work orders. Therefore if you want to expedite quantities smaller than 20 you have to give the appropriate instruction at each stage separately.

4. To use residual work-in-progress you may complete the work order quantity by expediting units from raw materials.

Write down the results:

BATCH-SIZE SYNDROME
Financial Results

Net profit	_____
Cash	_____
Return on investment	_____
Throughput	_____
Inventory	_____
Operating expenses	_____

Utilization of resources

Resource	% production	% set up
Blue	_____	_____
Green	_____	_____
Cyan	_____	_____
Magenta	_____	_____
Brown	_____	_____

Order Fulfillment

Product	Quantity required	Quantity delivered
A	_____	_____
D	_____	_____
F	_____	_____

If that was not enough to cause you to start despising the cost world I don't know what will.

Read carefully the following logical tree:

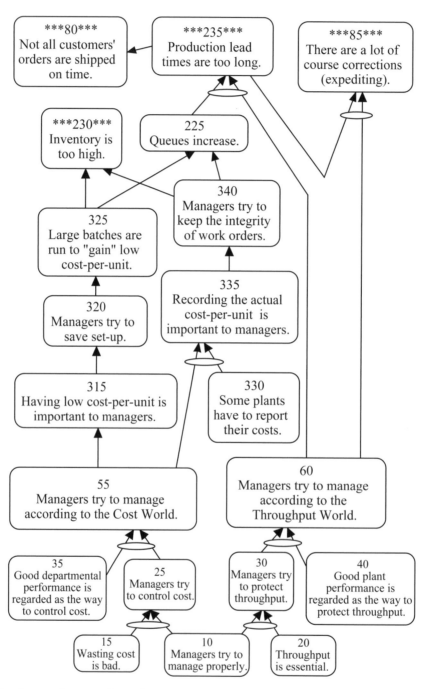

80
Not all customers' orders are shipped on time.

235
Production lead times are too long.

85
There are a lot of course corrections (expediting).

230
Inventory is too high.

225
Queues increase.

325
Large batches are run to "gain" low cost-per-unit.

340
Managers try to keep the integrity of work orders.

320
Managers try to save set-up.

335
Recording the actual cost-per-unit is important to managers.

315
Having low cost-per-unit is important to managers.

330
Some plants have to report their costs.

55
Managers try to manage according to the Cost World.

60
Managers try to manage according to the Throughput World.

35
Good departmental performance is regarded as the way to control cost.

25
Managers try to control cost.

30
Managers try to protect throughput.

40
Good plant performance is regarded as the way to protect throughput.

15
Wasting cost is bad.

10
Managers try to manage properly.

20
Throughput is essential.

Let's analyze what happens. The fact is that managers do try to manage also according to the cost world and therefore it's no wonder that it's important to them to have low cost-per-unit (315). That is the major reason that managers try to save set-up (320). The desire to save

68

set-up translates into the need to have large batches to "gain" low cost-per-unit (325). Some plants have to report their cost-per-unit to corporate or to an outside organization (330). For those organizations it is also important to properly record their actual cost-per-unit (statement 335) and therefore managers in such an operation will try to keep the integrity of work-orders (340).

Large batches and the attempt to keep the integrity of these batches both contribute to increasing queues (225) and to inflating inventory (230). Large queues unavoidably translate into longer lead times – so long that the throughput-world (because you still have to make money, you still have to deliver everything we promised to our clients) forces the recognition that they are too long (235). And then we have to start splitting batches and expediting (85). But it's too late, not all orders will be shipped on time (80).

Does the clash between the cost-world and the throughput-world lead to more devastating compromises? Unfortunately yes. Many more. But realizing, to the extent that we now realize, that these compromises are the major cause for our difficulties is enough. We have the base to start deriving the solution.

We do, but there is still something that bothers us. It bothers us to the extent that if we do not take care of it, it will hound us and impair our efforts later on. There is still the open issue of the role of the original list of reasons.

When guiding a group spend time discussing batching in their environment. Then use the following graph to talk about economical batch quantity. Many people have learned it, but it doesn't mean that they remember. We need them to understand it rigorously in order to develop their intuition about the way Theory Of Constraints is seeking non-compromising solutions. So don't skip it.

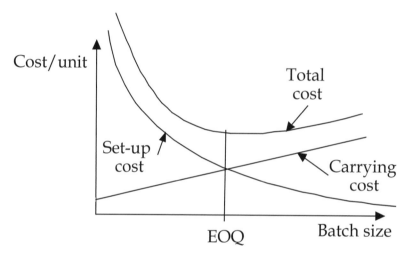

Then explain work-orders and why they make sense in an organization that thinks it has to report actual cost per unit. Skip this explanation and some people will have a hard time understanding the simulator. Then explain how to run 312 in the same way you learned it, including the summary and filling in the results in the tables. Give them one hour for the actual run. Don't fight those whose frustration from the deteriorating results causes them to refuse finishing the run.

When they finish, just summarize the deterioration in the results and then show the tree and meticulously explain the logic. That's important.

Then turn their attention to their original, it cannot be that this list doesn't play any roll.

10 THE ROLE OF THE ORIGINAL LIST OF REASONS.

There is still the open issue of the role of the original list of reasons. It cannot be that they are not important at all. They are important. But if we take care of the core problem – the compromises – they will become much less important. How come? Because those reason just   ADD FUEL TO THE ALREADY EXISTING FIRE!

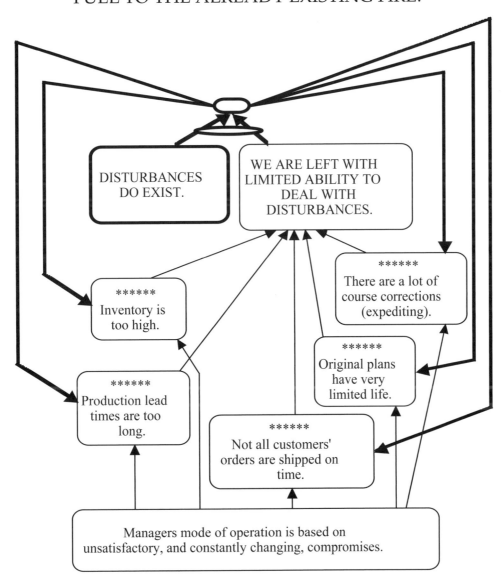

What we've already seen is that the compromises lead to a whole set of undesirable effects. They lead to piles of inventory and long lead times, to missing orders, to limiting the validity of plans and to constant expediting. All these undesirable effects contribute their share to limiting our ability to deal with disturbances. The original list is mainly a list that details the disturbances that do exist. The results of having those disturbances and not having enough ability to deal with them, loops back and amplifies each and every one of the undesirable effects.

For example, if our production lead-time is too long and on top of it, a machine breaks down, then more orders will be late. But what would happen if our production lead time would have been much shorter, shorter compared to the interval promised to the clients? In most cases we will have enough time to deal with a break down (unless it is a real catastrophe) without missing orders.

The disturbances are adding fuel to the fire, but maybe we can eliminate the fire. When we examined the feasibility, time and money needed to reduce the original list we saw that it is going to be a mammoth task. We now understand that if we take care of the need for compromises we can considerably reduce the bad impact of those disturbances, even if the disturbances themselves remain at the same level. Moreover, maybe by eliminating the compromises we'll create an environment where we will be able to systematically reduce the disturbances themselves.

In summary:
1. The compromises are a major reason for the existence of the undesirable effects.

2. The compromises create an environment which doesn't leave us enough ability (and time) to effectively deal with disturbances.

3. The compromises swallow the needed resources (time, money and management attention) to effectively reduce the source of the disturbances.

and maybe,

    4. The compromises create an environment in which it is difficult to objectively realize which source of disturbance should be dealt with.

So what are we waiting for? Let's see how we can, realistically, eliminate the need for these devastating compromises.

When guiding a group start by explaining the above tree. Use representative items from the original list of reasons to demonstrate the loops. Then summarize with the last four points. Take a break before diving into the solution.

It wasn't easy, it wasn't short, but we peeled the first layer of resistance. At this stage people are eager (some even enthused) to hear your suggested solution.

You haven't yet won the war, just a battle. If you notice, at the same time that they want you to explain your suggestion, they are skeptical. Skeptical to the extent that they are ready to challenge it, even before they know what it is. Take it as a good sign; you peeled the first layer of resistance. You are now facing the second layer.

"The second layer of resistance: arguing that the proposed solution cannot possibly yield the desired outcome. Your proposed solution looks obvious to you, yet it doesn't to others."

The key in introducing a solution (of course, after overcoming the first layer) is not to tell your audience the solution, but to cause them to re-develop it. Let see how it can be done.

A SOLUTION
PART TWO

The core problem is that managers must compromise between the cost-world and the throughput-world. We are looking for a solution, for an alternative. An alternative exists only if the conflict is not a MUST. Therefore, in looking for a solution, it will behoove us to emphasize the word MUST, re-examining if the conflict is really a MUST.

Let's revisit the core conflict – this time expressed in the terminology of MUST; the terminology of necessary conditions (rather than the terminology of sufficient conditions we have used so far in the trees).

It's easier than it sounds as is illustrated by the diagram on next page. The objective is given in statement A: "To manage properly". Statement B is: "Managers try to control cost." The arrow connecting statement B to statement A is a necessary condition arrow: In order to manage properly managers <u>must</u> try to control cost. Meaning that if cost is not under control we don't refer to the situation as properly managed .

Statement C is: "Managers try to protect throughput." The arrow between C and A indicates that C is a necessary condition for A. In order to manage properly managers <u>must</u> try to protect throughput. Both B and C are necessary conditions. Managers must fulfill both at the same time, otherwise the objective is not reached.

Assumptions underlying
the
basic dilemma

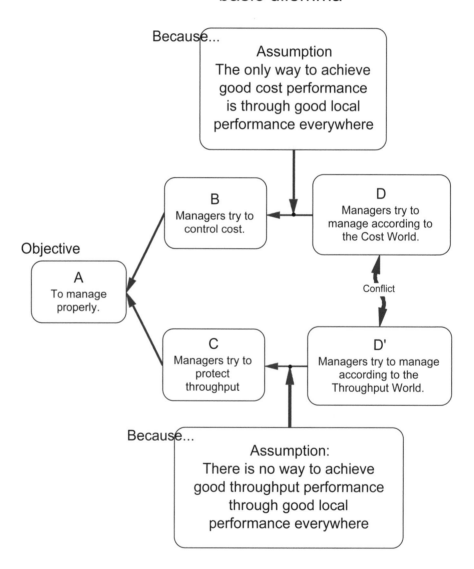

Now to the conflict. Statement D: "Managers try to manage according to the cost-world," is a necessary condition for B; in order for managers to try to control cost they <u>must</u> try to manage according to the cost-world. while statement D': "Managers try to manage according to the throughput-world," is a necessary condition for C; in order for managers to try to protect throughput they <u>must</u> try to manage according to the throughput-world

Which is the arrow we feel less confident about? Which of the necessary conditions are you willing to challenge? If you are like me, it's the arrow, "trying to manage according to the cost-world is a necessary condition for cost control." Let's examine the assumption underlying this arrow.

The claim is that in order for managers to try to control cost they <u>must</u> try to manage according to the cost-world. Why? Because we assume that the only way to reach good cost performance is through good local performance everywhere. Is the assumption correct?

Let's view our experience with the simulator. The difference between our first run of the simulator and our second run was that in the second run we strived for higher performance on each resource; we wanted higher efficiencies. No other differences. The resources were the same, products and tasks the same, everything the same. It's like having two identical twin plants, where in one we try harder to achieve good local performance. What an opportunity to check the validity of our assumption.

Examine the results you wrote of the first run and those of the second run, the one with the high efficiencies. Now answer the following questions:

1. Which plant shipped more finished products to the market - first run or second run?

[If you ran the second plant like the vast majority of managers, then towards the end of the week when you needed the cyan resources and the magenta resources to concentrate on finishing the orders for this week, they were busy fiddling around with the inventory you released for efficiency reasons. No wonder that in the second plant you probably missed more shipments. Think about it, this phenomenon must exist, and not just on the simulator. In real operations pre-release of work messes up the priorities to the point that even on resources which are not bottlenecks we have hot, red-hot and do-it-now jobs.]

2. In which plant were the resources more loaded - the first run or second run?

[The same thing will happen in the real world. Relatively high loads are to be expected for a real world operation if it operates under the efficiency syndrome. Even when there are not enough orders, we can almost always produce to forecast. And if pressured, workers and foremen can usually "massage" the numbers.]

In light of the above answers:
3. In which plant is there more pressure to hire/buy more resources?

[And in real organizations? If you ship everything on-time and the efficiencies of your resources are low, what chance do you have to convince headquarters to authorize the hiring of more people or approve the purchase of more machines? Not nearly as good as if the situation is the opposite.]

In the light of the above answer:
4. You ran two plants. In one you were allowed to run as you like, in the other you had to try to reach good local performance for each resource. In which plant were the costs more under control?

Now another set of questions:
1.   In which plant was there more inventory at the end of the week - the first run or the second run?

[And in real world operations? In real world operations there are very few constant bottlenecks. Striving to achieve high efficiencies on non-bottlenecks leads unavoidably to an increase in inventory.]

2. If you yield to the pressure and add resources, in which plant would the impact on the resulting inventory be bigger?

[As I have mentioned (and as you can check by the numbers) there is enough capacity in the Paradise Plant to produce the entire market demand within the week. Yielding to pressure to add capacity means to increase the capacity of non-bottlenecks.

In the first run, when you probably didn't even dream of releasing material just so the resources would not stay idle, the impact of adding capacity would be to shrink the lead time and more comfortably meet the orders. In the way you were forced to run the second time, this was not the case any longer. At this plant, more capacity would mean that you have to release more material. More material in the pipe-line means, of course, more inventory, but it also means larger queues. Larger queues means that the average lead time increases and there is a greater need to properly set the priorities. I doubt that adding more capacity will yield significantly more orders to be shipped on time.

In the light of the above answers:
3. In which plant will the costs be more under control?

What do you think now about the cost-world assumption that the only way to reach good cost performance is through good local performance?

What baloney!

If we want, as we should, to control cost we should probably do exactly the same thing we do to protect throughput: We must try to manage according to the throughput-world. There is no conflict. There was only an erroneous assumption.

Realizing that a problem stems from an erroneous assumption, is a sure sign that there is a powerful quick fix ready to be picked. Quick fix in terms of investments, not in terms of the paradigm shift required. Before we dive into the paradigm shift required to properly manage production, let's first practice on an example – the batch-size syndrome.

When guiding a group use a slide of the core conflict with the two assumptions to highlight the conflict in necessary condition terminology. Take your time and explain it slowly. That's the way to bring everybody to realize the direction of our solution; to realize that this time we are not offering an aspirin to deal with cancer. Allow them to have fun with the two sets of questions, encourage parallels to your organization.

When you reach the conclusion, go back to the core conflict to show that, most probably, our difficulties stem from a phantom conflict, from an erroneous assumption that prevail for so long in so many organizations. Summarize with the following:

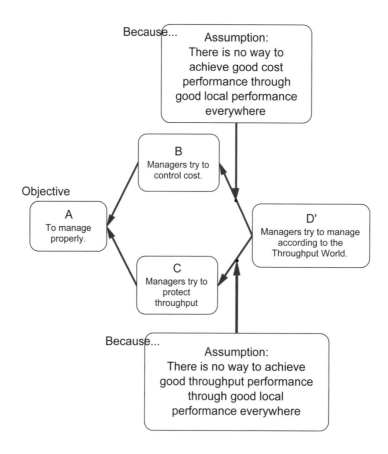

12 BATCHING

Let's review again the batch size dilemma as we understand it in the cost-world. Since the beginning of the 20th century, there have been literally thousands of articles and quite a few books devoted to polishing the batch-size compromise; to more precisely calculate the Economical Batch or Order Quantity (EBQ or EOQ) under various specific scenarios. (As far as I know, no one bothered to look at this dilemma from the throughput-world perspective, until recently.)

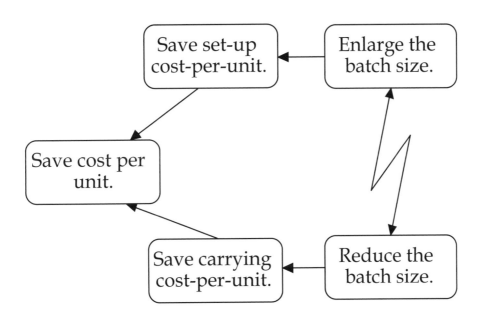

Now that you have run a (simulated) plant with and without the batch size restriction, you probably feel uncomfortable with the way the dilemma is presented. Use your understanding that we should not assume that local considerations always lead to global results, to formulate your questions about the dilemma.

Three such questions are raised on the dilemma:

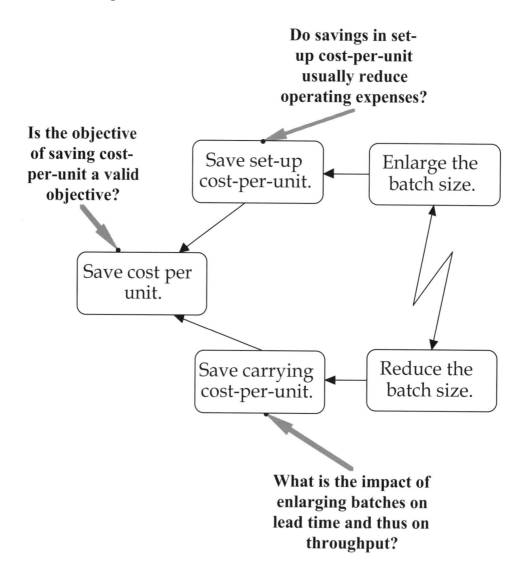

Do savings in set-up cost-per-unit usually reduce operating expenses?

Is the objective of saving cost-per-unit a valid objective?

Save set-up cost-per-unit.

Enlarge the batch size.

Save cost per unit.

Save carrying cost-per-unit.

Reduce the batch size.

What is the impact of enlarging batches on lead time and thus on throughput?

1. Should we consider saving carrying cost per unit as one of the two main concerns of the dilemma (the other being saving set-up cost per unit)?

Saving carrying cost per unit is presented as the main reason for not enlarging the batch size, since large batches increase inventory and thus increase the carrying cost of inventory.

We know, from our work experience and from the simulator, that there are other associated bad effects – much bigger ones. Large batches, at the same time (and for the same reasons) that they increase inventory, also increase the average production lead-time. In today's competitive market, long production lead times cause organizations to lose some orders and miss delivery on orders that they haven't lost ... yet.

Since the damage caused to throughput by long lead times usually eclipses the damage of inventory carrying cost, it looks like we honor a minor (cost) factor while ignoring the major (throughput) one. A typical mistake in the cost-world.

2. Do savings in set-up cost per unit usually reduce operating expenses?

Very rarely do organizations lay-off people because set-ups have been reduced. And if people are not laid-off, what cost is saved? Let's be more blunt. If a non-bottleneck (and most of the resources are non-bottlenecks) is wasting set-ups, as long as it doesn't turn into a bottleneck, we don't incur any additional cost. Usually.

It looks like, in the real world – as opposed to the cost-accounting world – saving set-up cost-per-unit has nothing to do with saving actual cost to the organization. Which raises another question:

3. Is the objective of saving cost-per-unit a valid objective?

If the saving are not savings in real cost and the damage to the bottom line through the lost in throughput is not taken into account by cost-per-unit then saving cost-per-unit is not a valid objective.

The requirements are not the things we should be concerned about, and the objective is not valid, but we still have a conflict. So let's re-write it.

The objective is to run production effectively. This is an objective that is much more tangible, and not in debate. What do we mean by 'effective'? Every production manager will agree that in order to run production effectively we must be careful not to turn a non-bottleneck into a bottleneck and, at the same time to be effective, we must reduce production lead-time.

The conflict stems from the fact that in order not to turn a non-bottleneck into a bottleneck, sometimes we must enlarge the batch size, while in order to reduce production lead time we must reduce the batch size. Here is the representation of the conflict:

The Batch-Size Dilemma
In The Throughput World

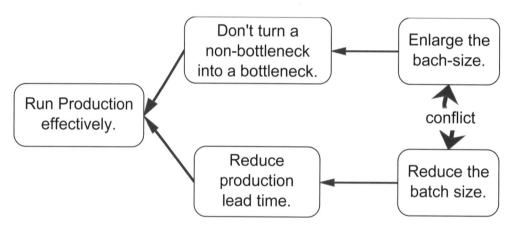

Getting rid of the artificial barrier of cost-per-unit, we now understand that for many parts when produced on non-bottlenecks we can reduce the batch size now. Many times, even halve it.

This will almost halve the average production lead-time! But continue cutting the batch sizes and sooner or later we'll reach the stage where further reduction of the batch size will turn resources into bottlenecks. Then how can we further reduce the batch sizes? One obvious way is to invest in reducing the set-up time itself, as JIT rightfully suggests (and provides the excellent methods to achieve dramatic reductions). Reducing the set-up time takes time and money. Is there a good quick alternative?

Yes there is. And you know it, at least intuitively. The problem is that until we precisely verbalize our intuition, we ourselves don't know how much we know and therefore we don't always use our know-how.

The way you ran the simulated plants indicates that you intuitively know a very good and quick solution to the batch size conflict. Simply compare the first run results to the third run, where the plant policy was to try and maintain the integrity of the batches.

In the first run, what batch sizes have you intuitively used? When you released material for F or E or A or C, what quantities did you release? Quantities in the range of 30 to 50 units. And when a resource was activated on a task, very seldom did you move that resource to another task before it finished the whole batch. In the first run you used, on average, larger batches than on the third run. Nevertheless the production lead times you demonstrated in the first run were by far shorter than in the third, units flowed much smoother and the results were much better.

How did you achieve this miracle? How did you succeed, in the first run, to process much larger batches while achieving much shorter lead times? Succeed to verbalize how you've done it on the simulator, and you'll be able to use it, more systematically, in your real life operation.

Here is another riddle that will help in the verbalization. Consider an assembly line or transfer line or process line (which ever you feel more comfortable with) dedicated to one type of product.

What is the batch size in a transfer line dedicated to a specific product? Answer: _____

Are you sure? Try again. Alternative Answer: _____

Both answers are right. How can it be?

_____

_____

_____

Imagine the units as they pass through the line. How many units are batched together before they are transferred to the next resource on the line?

Right, they are not batched together. Each unit, when it is finished being processed at one station/resource, is immediately passed to the next station/resource. The batch size is one.

But wait. There is another answer. In an assembly line dedicated to one type of product, how many units are done before we stop the line and set-up the resources to do another type of product? In a dedicated line, never (ignoring the life time of the product). Which means that the batch we run, until we do a set-up, is for all purposes, infinite.

So, for a dedicated line we have two correct answers, one and infinite. Something is wrong.

Yes, something is wrong, but not in our answers. Something is wrong in the question, "What is the batch size"?

Look again at how we arrived at the answer that the batch size is one unit. We interpreted batch as the number of units we batch together for the purpose of transferring them from one resource to the next. We have answered the question: "What is the size of the TRANSFER-batch?"

When we answered that the batch size is infinite we interpreted batch as the number of units a resource is doing before it stops, set-ups, and starts to work on another task. We have answered the question: "What is the size of the PROCESS-batch?"

Both interpretations are legitimate, but, as demonstrated by the example of the dedicated line, these two interpretations have nothing to do with each other. Transfer-batch and process-batch are so different that even when we talk about the same resource processing the same type of part, the two batches can coexist and have values as different as one and infinite.

You have done something similar in your first run. You didn't wait until the last unit of a process-batch finished at stage, let's say F1, before you moved units to be processed at F2. You intuitively used large process-batches and small transfer-batches simultaneously.

Now go back to the conflict:

No BATCH-SIZE-DILEMMA
In the Throughput World

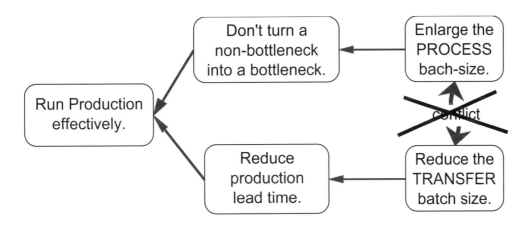

The necessary condition for saving set-up is to have large process-batches. The larger the process-batch the less the resource has to set-up. The necessary condition for reducing production lead-time is small transfer-batches. The smaller the transfer-batch the less time a unit has to wait before it's passed on to the next stage. Since the process-batch and the transfer-batch can be different and still coexist there is no conflict.

WE MET THE ENEMY; IT IS US. AGAIN.

Of course, another set of questions starts to blink red. For example, how should we report on actual cost when there is such an external requirement? How are we going to control the operation? How should we handle paper-work? Etc.

We'll be better able to answer these detailed questions after we answer the basic one: How come we didn't (don't) manage according to the throughput-world?

When guiding a group, use the Work Book, that appears as an appendix to this book, to bring them through the above chain of reasoning. Then start a discussion about the use of process and transfer batches in your organization. The first remarks from the group will be examples where it's already done. Examine them to see if you can improve. It won't be long before some members of the group will bring other examples where it should be done but it isn't. Some positive actions will result.

When the group starts to get bogged down by the open questions of how/what to do, suggest putting these questions aside until you unfold the entire logistical solution. And start the next topic.

13 THE THROUGHPUT-WORLD PROCESS

Where do we stand? We now understand that in order to protect throughput and control cost, in order to achieve each one and both together, managers must try to manage according to the throughput-world. There is no conflict. We must manage according to the realization that global results are not achieved through chasing good local results everywhere.

So what's the problem? Why don't we do it?

Because we don't know how. Because something essential is still missing.

In the cost-world managers at every level were under the impression that they knew what to do. This stemmed directly from the underlying concept of the cost-world; the concept that good global results are achieved through good local results everywhere. Each manager knew what to do, concentrate on his/her area of responsibility trying to achieve the best local results.

In the throughput-world this is not correct. As we said, the underlying concept of the throughput-world is that good global results are not achieved through good local results everywhere. But this is a negative statement, telling us what not to do. It does not tell us what to do. It does not give even a clue, to how a local manager should manage his/her area so that it will contribute the most to the global results.

What is missing is a focusing process. A process that will be powerful enough to provide clear direction to the organization as a whole, and to each department within it.

To derive such a process let's turn back to the chain analogy. We are interested in the strength of the chain. What determines the strength of a chain? The weakest link. So, if we want to improve the strength of the chain what must we do? What is the mandatory first step?

The first step must be to find the weakest link. There are no alternatives to that, no 'ifs,' no 'buts'. The first step is:

1. IDENTIFY the system's constraint(s).

'Identify' and 'constraint' are just more pompous words to say 'find' and 'weakest link'. We must appear respectable, mustn't we?

Suppose that we identified the weakest link. What now? If we want to strengthen the chain the answer is obvious. The only way to do it is to strengthen the weakest link. Nothing else will do.

Fine, but suppose that there are two ways to do it. Suppose that the weakest link is a machine that doesn't have enough capacity to meet demand – a bottleneck. In that case we can either squeeze the maximum from what we have, or we can purchase an additional machine. Of course we can do both, but which should we do first?

Since controlling cost is one of the two requirements of the throughput world the answer is obvious: Squeeze the maximum from the weakest link.
Or using more respectable words step 2 is:

2. Decide how to EXPLOIT the system's constraint(s).

So far we have looked only on the constraint. What about the other links, the non-constraints? Can we ignore them?

No, because the constraint does not operate in isolation, and in a chain linkages are not less important than the links. If we want to be able to exploit the constraint we'll have to manage the non-constraints in sync.

For example, suppose that the constraint is a bottleneck that can produce, maximum, 10 units an hour. The constraint is fed by another resource, a non-bottleneck, that also feeds other parts to other resources all being non-constraints. It turns out that this non-bottleneck is much more efficient at producing the other parts, the ones not required by the constraint. How many units an hour should the non-bottleneck produce for the constraint?

It doesn't matter if it is more efficient producing other parts, the answer is still ten units an hour.

And what about the efficiency of the non-bottleneck resource? It can be much more productive producing other parts.

No, by definition it cannot. Not if productive means doing what is good for the system as a whole.

This line of reasoning leads to the next step:

3. SUBORDINATE everything else to the above decision.

Before we continue let's understand the ramifications of this third step.

Suppose again that our constraint is a bottleneck that can produce, maximum, 10 units an hour, or the constraint is market demand that requires only 10 units an hour. Our non-bottleneck supplies these parts to the constraint. But it can easily produce 20 units an hour, and these type of units are all it can make. After a sufficient bank of protective inventory has accumulated, how many units an hour should this non-bottleneck continue to produce?

10 units an hour.

And what about the efficiency of the non-bottleneck resource? Producing only 10 units an hour when the resource can do 20 an hour means that its efficiency will be only fifty percent!

It doesn't matter.

It doesn't matter to whom? In most organization what happens to a department that reports efficiencies as low as fifty percent? The foreman's head will be chopped, or his/her peoples' heads.

And still the third step is absolutely correct. It requires a change in performance measurements, a change in behavior, but it is still correct.

On the third step is where the battle between the old, established, cost-world and the intuitively obvious throughput-world is fought. The cost-world is saying exploit each and every resource; the throughput-world is saying don't even think of it that way. Exploit only the constraints, subordinate everything else.

Your mind is probably drifting to how to do it. We'll discuss it at length later, but now, let's continue to develop our process. We have step three. What next?

The fourth step is relatively obvious. If the steps of EXPLOIT and SUBORDINATE were not enough to break the constraint, the time has come for more drastic (and sometimes expensive) actions:

4. ELEVATE the systems constraint(s).

Off-load to non-constraints (even if they are much less efficient at performing the tasks off-loaded.) Subcontract, or even buy, more capacity. Remember, if you want to continue improving the bottom line, you must elevate the constraint.

Is there another step? Back to the chain analogy. You strengthened the weakest link and the chain became stronger. You strengthened that link again and the chain became even stronger. You strengthened that link again and nothing happened! Why?

You are right. It is not the weakest link any more. So what should you do? You should find out what is now the weakest link. You should go back to step 1. That, however, will not be enough. As you are going to see, in the stages of EXPLOIT, SUBORDINATE and ELEVATE, you have instituted many procedures. All these procedures were based on the fact that something specific was the constraint. Now that it is no longer the constraint, all those procedures have to be re-visited, otherwise these procedures themselves might become the constraint.

5. If in a previous step a constraint has been broken, go back to step 1, but do not allow INERTIA to cause a system's constraint.

In fact, these five steps are actually the process of ongoing improvement. But we are going to concentrate on the first three steps, learning how to run operations according to the throughput-world.

The process is simple. Now let's get familiar with using it.

In guiding a group, ask them to use the chain analogy to cause the group to derive the steps. Make sure to draw it from them rather than telling it to them. In this way this 5-step process becomes what it is, intuitively obvious. We need people to have this conviction because the ramifications – the changes required relative to the cost-world – are significant.

14 EXERCISING THE PROCESS ON THE SIMULATED PLANT

1. IDENTIFY the system's constraint(s).

In the simulated plant, what are the system's constraint(s)? Maybe I should be more explicit. Suppose that you ran the simulated plant many times, until you developed the intuition that enabled you to score the maximum. What then are the simulated plant's constraints?

Write down you're answers:

In the simulated Paradise plant, what are the system's constraints?

1. _____

2. _____

What will be the constraint if we impose, like we have done in the second run, the efficiency syndrome on the situation?

_____

What will be the constraint if we impose, as we have done in the third run, the batch syndrome?

_____

Even without doing any calculations, after running the simulated plant once, you probably noticed that the Blue Resource is a constraint. It's not a bottleneck, it has enough capacity to supply the entire market demand, but it has no slack capacity to speak of. Not paying attention to that resource, not exploiting it, and you will not supply all the orders on time. We call it a Capacity Constraint Resource (CCR).

Have a look again at the details of the simulations:

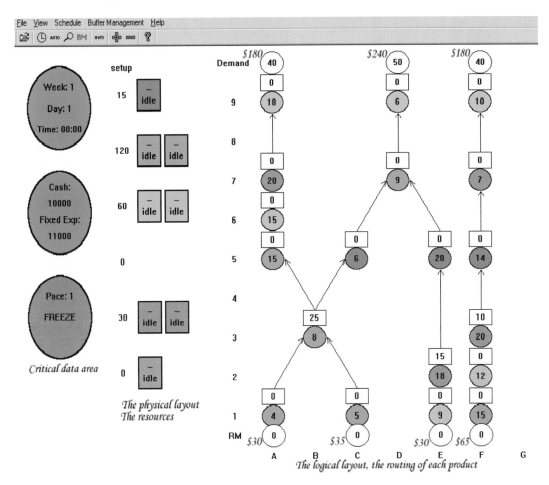

The Blue resource participates in producing products D and F. It is not needed at all for producing product A. What limits our ability to make more money from product A? The answer is we don't have enough market demand.

This is an example of a very common situation; a situation where we have two constraints. One is a Capacity Constraint Resource (CCR) and the other is market demand (for product A). We refer to CCRs, to market constraints, to vendor constraints as physical constraints.

However, your experience in the second and third runs show that many times we might have another type of constraint. In the second run and even more so in the third run, the limiting factor, the

95

constraint that limited operations from achieving better results, was a policy. Efficiency policy or batch-size policy.

We will assume that at least on the simulator, we don't have to obey such devastating policies. So the constraints are the Blue resource and market demand for product A.

How do you identify the constraints in a real life operation? We will discuss it later, once applying the whole process is much better understood.

2. Decide how to EXPLOIT the system's constraint.

Exploiting the system's constraint means not wasting it. In THE GOAL you will find much advice on improving the exploitation of a CCR, like staggering lunch breaks, etc. Unfortunately, in reality the biggest waste is that the capacity constraint resource is not working on what it should be working on. Deciding how to exploit a CCR first and most of all means that we decide, in advance, how we are going to use the scarce capacity of that resource. We decide in advance exactly which tasks, in what quantities, in which sequence, the constraint is to do the work.

At this stage, be careful not to be bogged down by scheduling all other resources in accordance. This belongs to the next step, to the subordination. Here, in step 2, we concentrate solely on the constraints.

Decide on the schedule for the Blue Resource. Fill in your decisions of how you are going to exploit the Blue resource in the simulated plant.

	Operation	Quantity
1.	_____	_____
2.	_____	_____
3.	_____	_____
4.	_____	_____
5.	_____	_____
6.	_____	_____

Now let's do it together.

What should the Blue resource work on at the beginning of the week? The Blue resource has three different tasks: C5, E5 and F5. There is inventory waiting in front of each of these tasks, so all are viable alternatives, right at the beginning of the week. Which one have you chosen? Why not another one?

Reality is that it doesn't matter which one of the three alternatives is chosen. The results at the end of the week will be the same. The important thing is to choose. That's important.

Suppose that you choose to start with F5. What quantity would you like the Blue resource to process? F has a market demand of 40 units, but before F5 there are only 10 units. Yes, the right choice is 10 units, obeying the first rule of management: Be paranoid. Right now there are 10 units. We don't want to schedule the Blue resource to do more than that in the hope that in the mean time we will bring more because if we don't succeed, we will not exploit the constraint. Be paranoid. (The second, not less important, rule of management is not to be hysterical. The art is to know how to distinguish between the two rules.)

So the first instruction will be process task F5, 10 units. And then? Then it should shift to another task where there is right now inventory ready. For example, the second instruction could be E5, 15 units. Because only 15 units are there.

And the third instruction? C5. How many? Since the parts coming from C5 are going to be assembled with parts coming from E5, you might decide to instruct the Blue resource to process only 15 units on C5 leaving the other 10 for product A.

To perform the first three instructions will take the Blue resource over 10 hours. In the environment of the simulator where the longest set-up is 2 hours and there are no breakdowns or scrap, 10 hours is eternity. Within 10 hours we can bring whatever part we want to be ready for the Blue resource.

It really doesn't matter what you decide the next instruction will be. What does matter, as we said already, is to decide.

We will now instruct the Blue resource to continue to work on F5. How much? 30 units, because that is what is left to complete the market demand for product F.

Now the next instruction can be E5, 35 units. Then C5, 35 units.

If we want to be sophisticated and really paranoid, we should reverse the sequence of the last two instructions. We should make E5 the last instruction. Why?

Suppose that sometime during the week – on Monday, Tuesday, it doesn't matter when–we have lost 5 hours on the Blue resource, for whatever reason. Since the Blue resource follows the sequence that we gave it, these 5 hours loss will impact us at the end of the week. Suppose that we have only two spare hours of capacity per week. This means we will be short three hours.

What are we not going to produce? The things that were scheduled to be processed in the last three hours. If we scheduled C5 to be the last production for the week, then we will not be able to process 30 C5 units – which will mean we don't ship 30 units of product D!

If instead we scheduled E5 to be the last operation of the week, this same three hours will result in not processing about 7 E5 units, which means we miss shipping about 7 units of product D. The disturbance, the of loss capacity on the Blue resource, was the same – loss of 5 hours. The damage to the performance of the organization was very different.

This is a fine example of the art of being paranoid, but remember that for our purposes it is not terribly important.

Right now the schedule for the Blue resource is the following:

	Operation	Quantity
1.	F5	10
2.	E5	15
3.	C5	15
4.	F5	30
5.	C5	35
6.	E5	35

3. SUBORDINATE everything else to the above decision.

The efficiency syndrome is still alive and kicking on the shop floor. For decades we hammered efficiencies into our work force: always being busy has become the work ethic. The problem is that this work ethic directly contradicts the third step. What is the work ethic we should institute in its place?

Do you recall the Road-Runner from the Warner Bros. cartoon? Beep-beep! It had two modes of operation. It either zoomed like a rocket, or stood still. This might be what we need. When a resource has inventory, let it work on it, as fast as it can. When it doesn't, it's okay to stay put. Working for the purpose of working does not help the organization. The goal of the company is to make more money, not to make its people sweat. Try to verbalize how a resource should behave.

THE "ROAD RUNNER" WORK ETHIC

_____

_____

_____

Beep, beep.

On the simulator, it is easy to institute such a work ethic. It is accomplished by clicking on the 'AUTO' command, it is the third icon from the left just below the main menu at the top-left. Resources will look for work and process it as fast as they can, but if there is no work they stay put.

The following picture shows the icons were the 'AUTO' icon is marked:

There is one exception to the freedom allowed to the resources. Common parts. We don't want the green resource to work on A5 just because there are parts. It may steal the work we have prepared for the Blue resource. So choose the option of "Restricted". Under this option the 'AUTO' instruction would NOT assign a machine to an operation that draws common part material. This means that whenever you want the green resource to process task A5, you will have to remember to assign it yourself by click and draw the machine unit onto the A5 circle.

Here is a summary of how to run the simulator according to the first three steps.

1. We identified the system's constraints:
They are the Blue resource and the market demand for product A - the free product.

2. We decided how to exploit the constraints:
The Blue resource schedule has been set to guarantee satisfying the market demand. We are going to pay particular attention that the Blue resource will follow this schedule without hic-ups. And we are NOT going to forget satisfying the market demand for the free product.

3. We are going to subordinate everything else to the above decisions:
The plant would work according to the 'AUTO' mode of operation.
We are not going to complicate our life with artificial work-orders.
Above all, our attention will be on the Blue resource and the free product, A.

4. We are not yet going to take any actions to elevate the constraints since we don't know if the Blue resource will continue to be a constraint (and we are not from marketing so we can not take actions to increase the demand for the free product).

But before you start the run, we should review why we expect the performance to improve (see diagram on the next page).

We have injected two new things into the mode in which we are going to operate the simulator. Material is released just to support the constraints (statement 10) and there are no artificial batch size practices (statement 20). Notice that these two statements are in sharp-edged boxes, which means they are not reality in most plants. They represent our suggested injections of how to operate in the throughput-world. Because of these two injections the result must be that there is no redundant inventory in the system (statement 30).

Another injection that we have decided on is that resources are not going to chase local efficiencies, but they are all on the road-runner ethic (statement 40). In our situation, except for the Blue resource, all other resources have ample spare capacity (statement 50) and because of it we expect two things to happen. One is that queues in front of the non-constraints will be relatively small (statement 60) and at the same time we logically expect that the queue in front of the Blue resource will guarantee its uninterrupted work (70). Smaller queues means production lead times are shorter (80) and it also means that we will need fewer course corrections (110).

We made sure that the Blue resource schedule is set to best meet market demands (90). That, together with statements 70 and 80, should lead to customer orders being shipped on time (100). And if they are, we will need less course corrections.

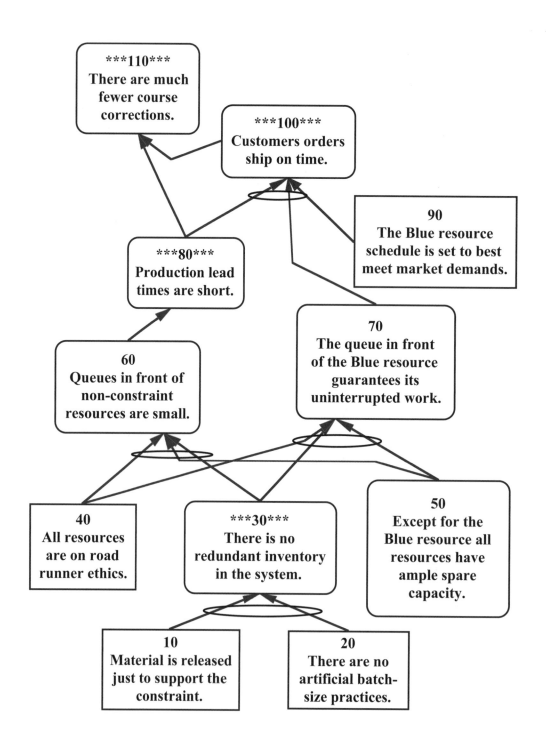

110
There are much fewer course corrections.

100
Customers orders ship on time.

90
The Blue resource schedule is set to best meet market demands.

80
Production lead times are short.

70
The queue in front of the Blue resource guarantees its uninterrupted work.

60
Queues in front of non-constraint resources are small.

40
All resources are on road runner ethics.

30
There is no redundant inventory in the system.

50
Except for the Blue resource all resources have ample spare capacity.

10
Material is released just to support the constraint.

20
There are no artificial batch-size practices.

We have high hopes now. Finalize your schedule for the Blue resource and for the shipping of product A (the constraints). Then run simulator 310 again.

Shipping schedule for product A:

    <u>Day</u>   Quantity

1. ____ _____
2. ____ _____

Try as hard as possible to adhere to the schedule you have decided on. If for whatever reason you have to deviate, don't give up on the schedule. Take corrective actions to get back to the schedule as fast as you can. If you don't, you have only yourself to blame for the results.

Record your results.

> *When guiding a group follow the same sequence you have read in this chapter. Pay particular attention to delivering the following important points:*
> > *1. Policy constraints are much more devastating than physical constraints.*
> > *2. The most important thing in exploiting a CCR is to decide, in detail, its schedule.*
> > *3. The road-runner ethic.*

Once they have performed the run, show them why deciding on the schedule and attempting to follow these decisions were so crucial. Even in a group of two you will have an example of how devastating it was to deviate from the predetermined schedule.

RUN RESULTS

Financial Results

Net profit	_____
Cash	_____
Return on investment	_____
Throughput	_____
Inventory	_____
Operating expenses	_____

Utilization of resources

Resource	% production	% set up
Blue	_____	_____
Green	_____	_____
Cyan	_____	_____
Magenta	_____	_____
Brown	_____	_____

Order Fulfillment

Product	Quantity required	Quantity delivered
A	_____	_____
D	_____	_____
F	_____	_____

15 DRUM-BUFFER-ROPE

The results you achieved in the last run were probably better than any previous results. And you probably felt much more in control. But, that's not enough. It's not enough because we cannot expect to get such results in a real plant where the visibility doesn't even come close to the visibility you have on the simulator. Running a real operation the same way you ran the simulator will, no doubt, improve its performance somewhat but it still leaves a lot of room for improvement. So if you haven't yet scored net profit above $4500, we can continue to find how to do even better. Otherwise please run the simulator again, but this time, to simulate real life pressures, raise the pace to 3 (immediately after you start the clock click twice on the '+', the seventh Icon from the left). Do it now.

You still scored quite well, but now we are in a position to determine what else should be done to guarantee even better results.

Write your observations of what went wrong in the last run and why.

1. _____

_____

_____

2. _____

_____

_____

3. _____

_____

_____

_____

You properly wrote things like:

Sometimes the Blue resource didn't have the right material (or any material) to work on.

Sometimes I released the material too late.

Some non-bottleneck resources were busy working on less important stuff and I realized it too late.

Examine your list again. All that you wrote is actually saying one thing: we haven't subordinated well enough, we haven't found exactly how to synchronize all other resources to support the schedule of the constraints. Here is where we can drastically improve, but....

How are we going to monitor all the other resources? How are we going to do it in a real plant where the visibility of what is going on is not even remotely close to what we enjoy on the simulator?

Maybe the answer hides in the observations that you've already made. Examine again the observations you wrote. They are not independent of each other. There are cause-effect relationships between them. Clearly verbalizing these cause-effect relationships will help us determine how we can best achieve effective subordination.

Next page shows an explanation for the emergence of negative effects:

At the bottom of the page there is a statement taken from our solution: material – type and quantity – is released just to support the constraints (statement 10). That I'm sure you have done. You didn't release material just so that the resources will score high efficiencies, and I'm quite sure that you calculated the quantities that have to be released for each type of material.

A Negative Branch

240
There is still the need for some course correction.

250
Some customers orders still are not shipped on time.

230
The Blue resource does not always have the right material to work on.

220
When the material is released too late resources are already busy working on less important tasks.

40
All resources are on road runner ethic.

210
The right material is released but some of it too late and some too early.

200
The timing of material release is not synchronized with the schedule of the constraints.

10
Material is released just to support the constraints.

But what about the timing of the releases? Allow me to speculate that the timing of the material released is not synchronized with the schedule of the constraints (statement 200). If so, statement 10 together with statement 200 leads to: the right material is released, but some of it too late and some too early (statement 210). You probably experienced this when you ran the simulator.

We put all resources on road-runner ethic (statement 40) and thus, when some needed material is released too late, at that time, resources are already busy working on less important tasks (statement 220). Which leads to: the Blue resource does not always have the right material to work on (statement 230). That caused you to take course corrections (statement 240) and in spite of them, if the deviations were severe, the end result was that some customer orders were not shipped on time (statement 250).

Putting it in this logical fashion highlights what must be done: we must deal with the root cause, we must eliminate statement 200, we must synchronize just the release of material with the schedule of the constraints. That's all. According to our logic tree, that should take care of the synchronization of all other non-bottleneck resources. What a relief, we don't have to chase each and every non-bottleneck, we just must make sure that the release of material will be synchronized with the schedule of the constraint.

Let's use an analogy to clarify to ourselves the essence of what we just proposed. Remember the boy scouts and Herbie from THE GOAL?

Since I was never a boy scout, but I was a soldier in the infantry, I will use the analogy of a troop of soldiers going on a march. It is a good analogy for a plant.

The first line of soldiers steps on virgin road – they process raw materials. Each line of soldiers continues to process the material until the last line is releasing the finished goods – the portion of the road that the entire troop has marched over. The distance between the first line of soldiers and the last one is work-in-process.

Does the army have any trouble controlling the performance of such a troop? Yes, of course. Look at the troop when it leaves the camp, all the lines are packed together. Then look at the same troop three miles down the road, they are spread across the countryside. Which means work-in-process climbed through the roof. To rectify it the officer will stop the troop, align the soldiers and start again. Stopping the soldiers means throughput is lost.

In the cost-world we were encouraging all the soldiers – including the first line – to walk as fast as they could. No wonder that gaps appeared almost everywhere. We try to rectify this situation by expediting; hot, red-hot, do-it-now, etc.

The assembly plants and the process industry found a much better way to control the troop. They mimicked the slave convoy. Since they couldn't afford work-in-process to be out of control they tied the soldiers to each other, they tied the resources with conveyor belts. In this way, work-in-process was limited. But there is a problem. Every time one of the soldiers drops his gun and is delayed to pick it up, what happens to the convoy? It stops. When a work center on a line breaks for more than two or three minutes, what happens to the entire line? It stops. That's why in lines (and in JIT implementations) it is mandatory to maintain very high reliability on each and every resource. Once you have achieved it, you are rewarded by the results.

Is there a better way? There must be a better way, if we believe that the five steps we have outlined are obvious, common sense. In the assembly line, or in JIT, we don't perform step 1 – we don't bother to identify the Capacity Constraint Resource, the CCR. Because of it we don't perform step 2 and 3. The problem is that we are violating step 3. What is the meaning of subordinate everything to the constraint? First of all, it means that a non-constraint is not allowed to stop a constraint. Is this prime condition obeyed in a line? No. So there must be a better way. The problem is to find it.

But we have just now found it. We have just declared that it will be enough to choke the materials release in accordance with the needs and timing of the constraints. It is like tying the first line of soldiers to the slowest soldier, forcing the first line to go not at its own pace but at the pace of the slowest soldier. This is equivalent to choking the release of virgin road to the first line so that their speed will be the same as the speed that the slowest soldier can process the road. We don't use any other ropes. What will happen?

THE BOY SCOUT ANALOGY

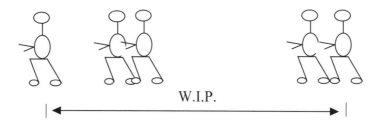

W.I.P.

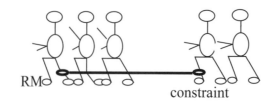

110

The first line of soldiers are, on average, faster than the slowest soldier. That's why the rope will usually be tight. When the rope is tight, the first line cannot possibly proceed at a speed which is greater than our slowest soldier. The other lines after them are faster than the slowest soldier, so they will be on the heels of the first line. There is no need for additional ropes. The lines after the slowest soldier, are faster than him, so they will be on his heels without using any ropes.

Where is the big advantage? Suppose that any soldier behind the slowest soldier drops his gun, and he is delayed picking it up. Will it effect the slowest soldier, will it stop him? No. So throughput is maintained. The sloppy soldier will pick up his gun and, being faster, he will close the gap. The only damage is a temporary blip in work-in-process. And if one of the soldiers in front of the slowest soldier drops his gun? As long as the slowest soldier did not close the gap in front of him, no harm has been done – not to throughput and not to work-in-process. Which means we have to decide on the length of the rope according to the sloppiness of the soldiers in the convoy. The more sloppy they are the longer the rope so that we guarantee a gap in front of the slowest soldier.

Basically what do we have here:

Drum - Buffer - Rope

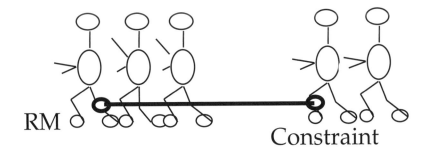

RM

Constraint

The slowest soldier dictates the pace of the entire troop (whether or not we like it). He dictates the DRUM beat for the entire convoy. We decide on a BUFFER, the length of the rope we are going to use - the amount of work we are going to release. And then we tie the ROPE, we choke the release of material to the gating operations, the first line, to be in line with the rate of the constraints.

In a real plant the situation is a little more involved than the linear troop of soldiers. The major difference is that troop has only one destination while a plant has to satisfy many products to many orders having different due dates. Moreover many times there is no CCR in a plant, the constraint is only the market demands. Therefore it will be easier to decide on a buffer for the whole plant – we call it the shipping buffer. It is like roping the first line of soldiers to the last line and by that guaranteeing that the maximum spreading will not exceed the length of the rope. Of course, if there is a bottleneck will tie the rope also to the slowest soldier.

The type and quantities of material released are in accordance with the type and quantities the constraints need (including the market constraints) according to the DRUM beat. The ROPE, the timing of the release of work, is a BUFFER time ahead of the time the constraints need the material.

If it is confusing it will be clear once we practice it on the example of the simulator. Let's start. We've already decided on the DRUM, we decided on the schedule of the constraints. Now, let's decide on the size of the BUFFER. How many hours in advance, of the time we need to ship the orders, should we release the corresponding material to the plant? In a real plant my strong advice is to choose the buffer to be equal to half the current lead-time. Yes, half of it. Remember, most of the lead-time is cause today by the efficiency syndrome and the way plants are dealing with batches. This is going to be changed so choosing half the existing lead-time is definitely on the size of being paranoid. But what is the conventional lead-time in our simulated plant?

So let's try to address it directly. What interval of time do we feel will comfortably enable us to do a product from start to finish? One day? Might be sufficient, might be a little rushed. Four days? A gross exaggeration, an exaggeration that will start to mess up the priorities of what is more or less important to be processed now. A number between the two extremes, 10 hours and 30 hours, will be good enough. You don't have to be precise here. As a matter of fact, since there is so much noise in the system, so many small and large disturbances, there is no point in trying to be precise. As every statistician (and physicist) will tell you: never try to optimize inside the noise. So we will choose twenty hours. Why not twenty five or fifteen? Be my guest.

In our simulated plant there is a CCR so will have to decide what portion of the SHIPPING BUFFER (the overall buffer we just choose) we'll allocate to protect the CCR. Since our CCR – the blue resource- is about in the middle of the process let's allocate to it half the buffer – 10 hours. Again there is no need to be precise, the performance of the plant are not impacted by small modifications in the buffer size, so if you want to choose 12 or 8 hours please do so.

Now, we have to tie the ROPE. We use the drum, the schedule of the constraints, as a base and using our choice of buffers, derive from it our material release schedule. In the next page we provide the full ROPE schedule based on the Drum. Let's go over it.

Our first drum operation is task F5, 10 units. How much material do we have to release for that? None. The material is already there, waiting for the Blue resource. The same holds true for the second and third instructions for the Blue resource–the material is already there. But when we come to the fourth instruction, F5, additional 30 units, these 30 units we have to release. They are not yet in the plant. When do we have to release them? 10 hours before the Blue resource is supposed to start processing them. That's the meaning of deciding on a CCR buffer size of 10 hours. To find out when to release the material, we must estimate when the Blue resource will finish its first three instructions (for which it has already the material) and reach the fourth instruction.

The Blue resource will start on its first instruction at time 0. It will take him approximately 2 hours to process 10 units at F5. There is no need to be precise here because we were not precise on setting the buffer size. Approximations will certainly do. Then, it will take the Blue resource an additional 8 hours to perform his second instruction,

E5, 15 units. And then the third instruction will take roughly 2 hours. This means that the resource will reach the fourth instruction about 12 hours from the start. At that time the material should already be there. We decided that if we release it 10 hours before it is needed, it will be sufficient, so we should release raw material F, quantity 30, at hour 2 (12-10=2).

Shipping Buffer Time = 20 Hours.
CCR Buffer time = 10 hours

Blue Resource Schedule   Material Release Schedule

	Operation	Quantity	Approx. Starting time	Raw Material	Quantity	Time
1.	F5	10	00:00	-	-	-
2.	E5	15	02:	-	-	-
3.	C5	15	10:	-	-	-
4.	F5	30	12:	F	30	2:
5.	C5	35	20:	A,C	35, 35	10:
6.	E5	35	23:	E	35	13:

Product A Shipping schedule

	Day	Quantity	Start time	Raw Material	Quantity	Time
1.	1	10	16:	-	-	-
2.	4	30	32:	A,C	30, 30	12:

We calculate when to release the material for the fifth and sixth instructions of the Blue resource in the same way. It will take the Blue resource approximately 8 hours to process F5, 30 units. Which means that the fifth instruction, C5, 35 units, will start roughly at hour 20. We need to release the corresponding raw materials 10 hours before, which means at hour 10. What are the corresponding raw materials?

It's not just material C, we have to release material A as well since the materials needed for C5 are sub-assemblies composed out of raw material A and raw material C. So, to satisfy the fifth instruction we have to release material A and material C, 35 units of each, at hour 10.

It will take the Blue resource roughly 3 hours to perform the fifth instruction, which means that the sixth instruction is scheduled to start at about hour 23. We need to release the corresponding raw material 10 hours ahead. Thus we should release material E, 35 units at hour 13.

We haven't finished yet. The Blue resource is not the only constraint. The market demand for A is another constraint. Out of the 25 units available right after B3 we are going to use 15 for the Blue resource. The other 10 we are going to use for product A. We'll ship them as soon as they're finished, at the beginning of the week. But the demand for product A is 40 units. We need another 30. When are we planning to ship them? We can wait until the last minute, until the end of day five, but remembering the rule about being paranoid, we'd prefer to be ready to ship them at the end of the previous day (there is no need to wait until the last minute and by that taking the chance of making something which is not urgent, urgent). The end of day 4 is hour 32. Obeying the length of the SHIPPING BUFFER, this means we must release additional raw materials A and C, 30 each, at hour 12.

No, we still haven't finished tying the rope yet. Our plant is a little bit more complicated than the linear case of a troop of soldiers. We have common parts inside the process. On the next page we present a negative impact that may happen if we neglect to deal with this.

All resources are on road-runner ethic, and to avoid "stealing" resources were not allowed to take initiatives on common parts (statement 300). Unfortunately, sometimes, we are late at giving permission to work on common parts (310). If that happened to you during your run you know the results. Some non-constraint resources became unnecessarily over-loaded for a while, which caused two undesirable effects: there was need for some frantic course corrections and some customer orders were not shipped on time.

Another Negative Branch:

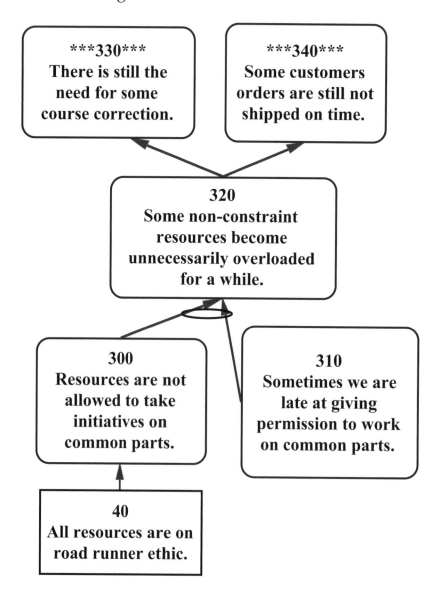

We have to tie the rope not just to the release of raw materials but also to the release of permission to work on common parts. In our simulated plant, the only problem is with A5.

If you are using the schedule that we used here as an example, the first 10 units for A5 are ready at the beginning of the run, so give permission for the green resource to work on A5 at time 0, and limit it to 10 units by clicking on A5 and write 10 instead of the default 9999. The other 30 units we have scheduled to be shipped around hour 32. Obeying the shipping buffer, we are going to release the material 20 hours before, at hour 12. You should give the green resource permission to work on A5 sometime after that, but to keep things simple give the permission at the same time you release the material, in most cases it does not make a real difference.

Add the schedule for permission for common parts:

'Permission to Work' Schedule:

	Operation	Quantity	Approx. Starting time	Raw Material	Quantity	Time
1.	A5	10	00:00	-	-	-
2.	A5	30	12:	-	-	-

Pay attention that when you activate the Blue resource on C5, you give it the appropriate limit.

If you chose another Drum or different size buffers, do the same calculations for the schedule you have chosen and the buffer sizes you have elected. You are now ready to operate the simulated plant according to DRUM-BUFFER-ROPE (DBR). Go.
Write down the results:

Run Result

Financial Results

Net profit	_____
Cash	_____
Return on investment	_____
Throughput	_____
Inventory	_____
Operating expenses	_____

Utilization of resources

Resource	% production	% set up
Blue	_____	_____
Green	_____	_____
Cyan	_____	_____
Magenta	_____	_____
Brown	_____	_____

Order Fulfillment

Product	Quantity required	Quantity delivered
A	_____	_____
D	_____	_____
F	_____	_____

When guiding a group, you will find out that the students don't have any difficulty with the concepts. Some might have difficulty with the calculation of tying the rope. Be patient. Computers have ruined our intuition for these simple tasks. Go slowly over the calculations on the standard schedule and then ask each one to do it on his/her schedule. If they have elected to use the standard schedule, make them change something, like changing the CCR buffer to 8 hours and re-do it. Check their work before they start to run.

When they are running the simulator make sure you highlight to each and every one that s/he is much more relaxed running the simulator. That now, when they know which local point to control (release and constraint) the same plant that drove them almost crazy in the first rounds, is almost boring. Equate it to the amount of fire-fighting and expediting in a real plant. You don't have to remind them to write their results. At this stage everyone is proud to record them. Then proceed according to the following page.

Not bad, not bad at all. But we can do even better. In a real plant we can talk to the resources! Since we have prepared the material release schedule, in a real plant we don't have to release the instructions one at a time in real time. We can give this list at the beginning of the week to purchasing and ask them to follow it. Just make sure that they don't release the material ahead of the time, but close to the time that is written and always in the specified quantities.

The permissions to the green resource (to work on the common part) we don't have to give on-line. We don't have to always keep ourselves alert. Rather we can give the schedule of the permissions to the person in charge of the green resource. If you notice, these schedules are not what we are used to. They are not schedules to be beaten. They are schedules of do-not-do-it-before. If you haven't implemented the road-runner concept, if the efficiency syndrome still exists, it won't work.

And what about the DRUM schedule? The obvious thing to do is to give it to the person in charge of the Blue resource, telling him/her,

"Try to follow it as much as you can. Try even to beat it. If you cannot perform any instruction for whatever reason, jump to the next instruction and return to complete the missing one at the first possible opportunity."

This will leave us with nothing to do. Not true. This will leave us with time to monitor the plant, time to see when and where we have to intervene due to a disturbance. Actually, we can simulate this beautiful scenario on the simulator. There is a way to give the full schedule of instructions to the relevant resources at the beginning of the week.

Restart the simulator. call params. 310, then click on the second Icon from the left, the one that shows a clock: .

You are now coming into the scheduling window:

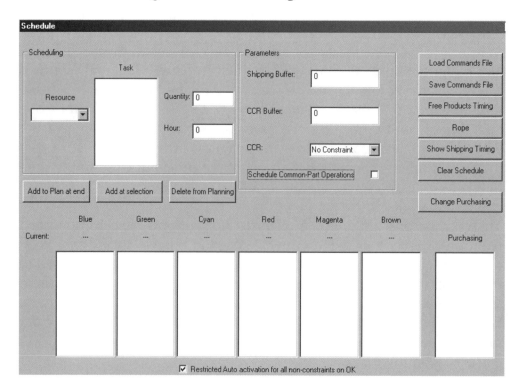

On the right hand of the window you have a column of buttons. The upper one is: Load Command File. This allows you to bring up a prepared list. Click on that button. You face now a list of command files, all of them start with 'commands.' Double click on 'commands.910'.

The instructions for the blue resource, the purchasing instructions and even the A5 permissions are all appearing. At the bottom you see marked the option to have all non-constraints on restricted auto activation. Click OK to return to the main window.

Next you might wish to settle the pace before you start running. You won't have much trouble with a pace 3, you clicking twice on the '+' icon would set it. Now, click to de-Freeze to start running. You have actually given all your instructions to the resources. What is left for you to do now is to watch carefully what is happening.

Control your impatience, don't interfere. If the schedule makes sense, and the buffer we have chosen is roughly right, everything we have released is roughly the same priority. So, it shouldn't matter which sequence the resources are choosing (and they are choosing according to the old, non-relevant rule of picking the biggest pile first).

Pay particular attention to where you are concentrating. In the real world Murphy does exist. What do we have to carefully watch in order to be on top of things? Try to verbalize it in clear sentences:

_____

_____

_____

_____

_____

It will be the base for the control mechanism that we need so badly in a real plant where disturbances do exist. The mechanism we call Buffer-Management.

16 BUFFER MANAGEMENT

Exploit the constraints. That's the key. As long as we succeed at that, the throughput of the organization is protected. No wonder that, when you watched the plant running itself, you intuitively concentrated on two points.

1. You, all the time, checked to see if the right material was flowing to the Blue resource. Whenever the bank of work in front of the Blue resource got low, you were itchy. Whenever it was almost full you felt relaxed. Rightfully so.

2. You watched the market constraint to see whether or not the products were moving toward the market to be shipped.

You did the right things, but how can you do it in a real plant, were the visibility is much lower and the disruptions are much higher then in our simulator? We'll have to cast what you did into some sort of a formal procedure.

At any given point in time you were looking to see if things are in line with what should happen next. But what is the window of future time, the horizon you we concerned about? The near future was your prime concern, the remote future was less relevant. Can we define 'near future' and 'remote future' a little more precisely? The answer is yes, since we know that the maximum window you should be concerned about is defined by the size of the buffer. Simply because anything beyond this window is not of any concern, since work that has be done beyond the buffer size is not even suppose to be released to operation. So we have a good clue; 'remote future' is an interval of time which is smaller but not much smaller than the size of the buffer and 'near future' is an interval which is relatively small compare to the size of the buffer.

Let's try to formalize it. The first third of the buffer we'll call Region I. Suppose that we are at time 12.5 hours and the buffer is 10 hours. Region one is the interval between the current time 12.5h and hour 16. What is of prime concern is the work the CCR is scheduled to do in that immediate future (between hour 12.5 and hour 16). We would like this work to be already waiting in front of the Capacity-Constraint-Resource, the blue machine. We don't want too many surprises there because to recoup means frantic expediting. The second third of the buffer we call Region II. The last third, Region III. We do not expect to find in front of the CCR much of the work it is scheduled to do at that time interval (hour 19 to hour 22.5).

To enhance your understanding let's take another example. Suppose that for another plant we decided on CCR schedule as given by the table.

	Operation	Quantity	Approx. Starting time	Approx. end time
1.	A	10	00:00	05:
2.	B	30	5:	17:
3.	C	24	17:	23:
4.	D	11	23:	34:
5.	E	10	34:	37:
6.	C	75	37:	55:
7.	A	20	55:	65:

The buffer is set to be 15 hours, and materials are released in accordance. If the current time is 0, the tasks that we expect to be right now in front of the CCR – Region I tasks – are only task A. Buffer tasks – tasks that have been released to operations – are A and B. Nothing else has been released. After 5 hours, when the current time is 5, Region I tasks will be B, while the buffer tasks will be B and C. Fill in the Region I task(s) and buffer tasks for each specified current time.

Current time	Region I tasks	Buffer tasks
0	A	A,B
5	B	B,C
10		
15		
20		
25		
30		
35		
40		
45		

If you noticed, this bank of work is not the regular inventory buffer. The content, the type of parts, which are held in this buffer changes according to the schedule of the constraint. What we are trying to hold there is not specific parts but a specific number of hours of work. And not just any work, but the work that we have decided that the constraint should work on. That's why we explicitly call this buffer, a time buffer.

Now, let's turn our attention to the very important issue of control. For that we have to introduce another useful term, "hole in the buffer." A hole in the buffer means work, which is scheduled to be done by the constraint within the buffer period of time, is not yet waiting in front of the constraint. To better understand the concept of "holes" try to answer the following questions:

In the previous example, suppose that a non-constraint (feeding the CCR) breaks down, and stays down, when it processes E.

At what time does task E becomes a HOLE in region III?

_____

At what time in region II?

_____

At what time in region I?

At what time does it penetrate through region I?

What are the rules of control? Somebody should monitor the content of the inventory waiting for the constraint and match it to the upcoming schedule of the constraint. Preferably this somebody should be the person in charge of the area of the constraint. In a minute you will see his/her incentive to do so.

In terms of control his/her job is to highlight the holes in the buffers, displaying (for every other person in operation) which task and quantity are holes in Region I and in Region II. This display is the actual priority of all other non-constraint foremen; if they have doubts about what they should do next, the depth of penetration of the hole in the buffer determines the priority. For example, if a foreman of a non-constraint is holding two tasks, one which represents a hole in Region II and another which represents a hole in Region I, he/she should first concentrate on completing the second task. This is true for all resources, including maintenance and tooling.

This way the burden of chasing down the parts is removed from the shoulders of the person in charge of the constraint (or the expeditor) and passed on to the non-constraint supervisors. In order to guarantee proper exploitation of the constraint we prefer that the person in charge will be there, rather than running around chasing work. Will the other managers collaborate? Put yourself in the shoes of the manager in charge of maintenance: today, how does he/she set priorities when three different people are coming to him complaining about three different breakdowns? The best he can do is to decide by the volume of the complainers. If he/she has access to the information about the depth of penetration of the holes into the buffers, the priorities are clear to him/her and to everyone who approaches him/her.

Behaving this way means that most expediting is done (if you can call adjusting to the right priorities - expediting) by the line managers themselves, not by the expediters. Still, the expediters are playing a major role. Whenever a hole appears in Region II, they track down the missing items. Maybe they haven't been released because of some problem in purchasing. Maybe they are stuck at a resource because of a problem. They track it down, note it, and plan an emergency action, but don't yet implement it. Only when the hole penetrates into Region I do you take the action.

Let me make sure we understand. When a hole penetrates into Region I it is an emergency. You cannot afford the luxury of only then tracking down the problem and planning the corrective actions. This must be done when the hole was in Region II. The minute the hole penetrates into Region I, that is the time to expedite. Still, don't even dream of expediting when the hole is in Region II – most of those holes will be taken care of in the natural mode of operation and if you interfere, you will throw the operation into chaos.

You may get the impression that most tracking of holes in Region II will not lead to any action. This is correct as long as we are talking about day-to-day actions. But these efforts are not wasted, they do lead to other not-less-important-type of actions. Suppose that you compose a list of where the missing items were found. Such a list made over just one week will tell you vital information. You will find out that most of the missing items were found in very few places. These are the places where you should concentrate your improvement efforts. It might be an unreliable set-up on a particular resource, it might be a quality problem in a particular process, it might be an unreliable vendor. Use LEAN techniques to correct the problem. Once it is corrected, there will be fewer deep holes in the buffer, which means you can reduce the buffer size – leading directly to less work-in-process and shorter lead times.

In Summery, the Buffer Management is not only an essential tool for enabling supervisors to exercise self control and enabling plant managers to take corrective actions before the damage is done, but it is also the focusing mechanism for all LEAN local initiatives.

You probably noticed that throughout this chapter, whenever I used an example I used the word CCR. Otherwise I used the word constraint. Buffer management is done not only for the CCRs but for the market constraint as well. The shipping buffer is as essential as a CCR buffer. This time you do not monitor according to the future work of a resource but according to the schedule of shipments. For example, a hole in Region I of a shipping buffer means that within the next 3 hours (assuming that you have chosen the shipping buffer to be 10 hours) there is a shipment scheduled and the goods are not yet in the shipping department and have not been shipped.

To see the extent that Buffer management is helpful run again the simulator, load the command file and click on the 'BM' icon. It is the fifth from the left on the icon line. Two 'traffic lights' are now displayed at the bottom-left part of the screen. One is called 'CB', and it stands for the CCR Buffer. The other is 'SB', the Shipping Buffer.

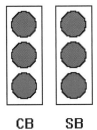

CB   SB

Now run. At the start the traffic lights are Green. That means that there are no holes in region II or I, not for the CCR or the Shipping dock. But, with time the light might change to yellow (Hole in region II) or even red (hole in region I). Click on that circle and a windows opens with the necessary information about what is missing.

When BM is activated the simulator follows its logic in the sense that non-constraint do obey the additional information provided by holes in the buffer. When a hole appears in region I (and a red light is on) the resource that is suppose to work on the missing part will stop anything else it is doing and switch to do the urgent task. To realize the power of it you may elect to run the simulator again and again testing the extent to which Buffer Management enables the reduction of the buffers and with it the inventory and lead time of the plant.

In real life plants, where the visibility of the information is far from the paradise we have in the simulator, and where disturbances are by far bigger (remember the original list of complaints?) the impact of using buffer management is dramatic. Experience shows that Buffer Management almost doubles the results relative to using only Drum-Buffer-Rope. With today computer technology, when so many plants do have computers at every production department it is a gross mistake not to establish Buffer Management.

 Now, let's discuss another important topic. What happens when, due to a change in the mix of orders, the CCR changes? Usually, chaos. But, if you have buffer management, you will notice it immediately. Please, answer the two questions :

> 1. Suppose a new, unrecognized, CCR is feeding the old CCR. What will be the impact on both the buffers?

_____

_____

_____

_____

> 2. Suppose a new, unrecognized, CCR is NOT feeding the old CCR. What will be the impact on both the buffers?

_____

_____

_____

_____

Write down your answers before you continue reading.

In the first case, holes will appear in the CCR buffer penetrating more and more into Region I. As time goes by and you have not taken any corrective actions, the holes will cross Region I – which means the CCR will consistently face a situation where it is supposed to work on these tasks and the materials are not there. It won't take long before the CCR creates holes in the shipping buffer. In the second case, holes that penetrate through Region I will consistently appear only in the shipping buffer.

In both cases, when you track back to the source of the holes (searching to see where the material is stuck) you will find the new CCR. The supervisor will immediately tell and convince you that s/he simply doesn't have enough capacity to cope with the load.

Buffer management is a very good mechanism to track the emergence of new CCRs. It is also a very good mechanism to find the CCR when you first start. Arbitrarily choose a work center as a CCR and implement Drum-Buffer-Rope and Buffer Management. If you chose the wrong work center, the true CCR will stick out like a sore thumb in just a few days. This is probably the fastest way to find the CCR in environments where there is no clear consensus or where management is under the impression that the CCR is moving from one department to another every day or two.

Now start the discussion about the following points:

1. Holes in the buffers as the prioritizing scheme for all line manages.
2. When to expedite and when not.
3. Focusing local improvement activities.
4. Tracking change in the CCRs.

If in your organization people do not have a consensus about which work center is the CCR in their plant guide them to realize how just picking a resource as a trail CCR implementing and implementing Buffer Management will lead to a fast and unequivocal determination of where the CCR actually is.

17 THE V, A, AND T CONFIGURATIONS

At this stage the methods of Drum-Buffer-Rope and Buffer Management are conceptually understood, but practice is vital. Activate the simulator on plant 350 (restart the simulator, and double click on 'params.350'). The layout is hereby displayed. It's the same type of plant we have been running, but a little more complicated. You have only one run to score a very good result, so take your time and plan your actions.

Identify the constraints. Exploit them – determine a reasonable schedule for them. Tie the ropes. And when you are ready, run the simulation.

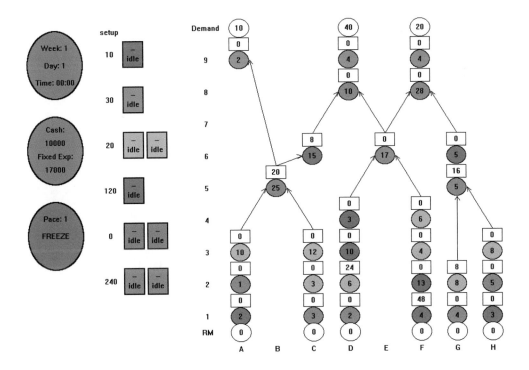

Now you are in a position to evaluate how much you have learned. What do you think you would have scored if this was the first time you ran the simulator, before you learned about DBR and Buffer Management?

So far we have examined only one type of configuration. Both plants 310 and 350 are what we call A-type plants, where many parts are processed and then assembled into relatively few products. Let's get familiar with the other, quite different, types of plant configurations.

Here is another type. Call Params.360 to bring it on your screen.

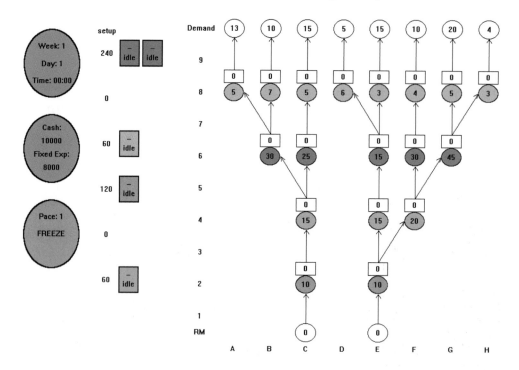

This is what we call a V-shaped plant, for obvious reasons. Almost all base industries belong to this category (for example, the steel industry). The dominant constraint in plants with this shape is the efficiency syndrome, in each and every department. The tree, next page, outlines the characteristics of the common problems in such an environment.

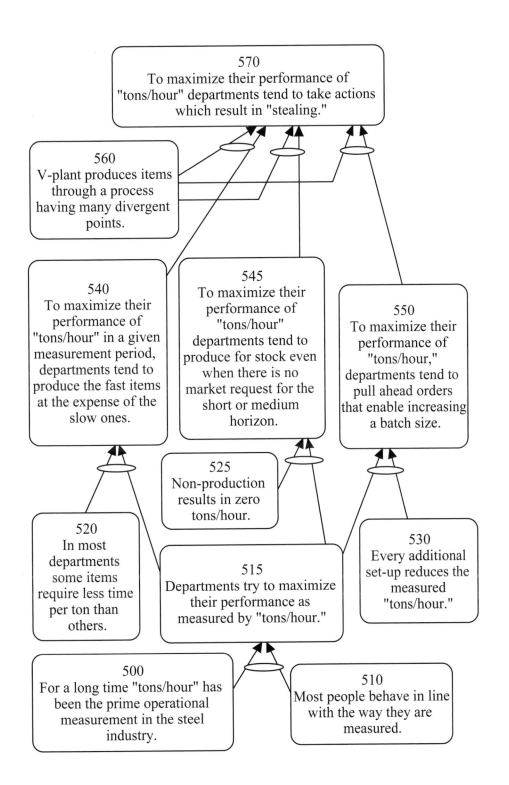

In the steel industry, each department is judged according to how many tons they process per hour; the measurement of tons/hour is the prime operational measurement (statement 500). We all know that people behave in line with the way they are measured (510) and therefore, in the steel industry, it's no wonder that departments try to maximize their performance as measured by tons per hour (515). What does this lead to? On its own, it might make sense, but not when combined with other facts which exist in that industry. Like the fact that in almost all departments some items require less time per ton than others (520). For example, to produce 10 tons of 2″ thick plates takes much less time than to produce 10 tons of 1/2″ thick plates. The result is that in order to maximize their performance of tons/hour in a given measurement period, departments tend to produce the fast items at the expense of the slow ones (540). You can imagine what this leads to–high inventory of the fast items while missing orders on the slow items.

In the steel industry, significant set-up times exist in every department, and as everybody knows, setup reduces the tons/hour–simply while you are doing the set-up you produce nothing (530). As a result, to maximize their measurement of tons/hour, departments tend to pull ahead orders to increase the batch size (550). Once again it leads to unnecessarily high inventories and unreliable due date performance.

The worst situation for a department is to be idle, non-production results in zero tons/hour (525). It's no wonder that to maximize their tons/hour departments tend to produce (to stock), even when there is no market request for the short or medium horizon (545). This definitely doesn't help the inventories.

But now we are coming to the real killer. In V-shaped plants, items are produced through a process having many divergent points (560). Combine this with each of the facts outlined in 540, 545 and 550 and what do you get? You get that to maximize their performance of tons/hour departments tend to take actions which result in "stealing." For example, we prepare the steel for a near term order of 60″ wide plates. The slitting department, produces more tons/hour when the plates are wider. So, if there is some order for 70″ wide plates on the horizon, the slitting department, to boost its near term performance, might use the steel to produce 70" wide plates. What are our chances of delivering the 60" order on time?

To see how out-of-control this situation is, run simulated plant 360. The eagerness to score high on tons/hour will be simulated by encouraging each resource to produce as much as it can – you can activate the machines not by using the 'AUTO' feature, but by simply drag-and-drop from the machine unit to the task – and you are not going to use the Limit option. To stop a resource from over producing you either move to another task or click on the operation and put 0 on the limit. Plan carefully, and when you are ready, start the simulation.

This run will give you some intuition into the damage and frustration resulting from "stealing." By the way, you may notice that in this simulated plant resources do breakdown now. The timing of the breakdowns was not planned to make your life particularly difficult – it is done by a random number generator. You may blame the breakdowns, but the core problem is the stealing. Record the results when you have finished.

Now, let's run this plant using DBR, in full, which means that resources will be restricted by the rope from taking raw materials or common materials ahead of time. To achieve a successful implementation in reality it's not enough to just provide the DBR schedules. The prime measurement must be changed. It should not be tons/hour but rather the magnitude to which a department has created holes in Region I of the buffers. This is important. You cannot instruct people to do things one way and then measure their performance based on a contradictory measurement. Actually, you can, but then don't expect results.

Let's choose the Blue resource as the CCR – this resource has the highest load of process and the longest set-up time. Let's determine a drum – the schedule for the Blue resource. Since all orders must be fulfilled by the end of the week, it doesn't matter in which sequence we schedule them on the drum. For example, let's arbitrarily decide to schedule from left to right. The Drum will be:

B6, 23 units
C6, 15 units
E6, 20 units
F6, 10 units
G6, 24 units

Now we have to decide on a Buffer. What number do you like? The set ups are a few hours, and there are breakdowns, so a buffer time of 5 hours might be too small. 10, 15 or 20 hours looks okay. Let's use 10 hours.

Now we have to tie the Rope – to generate the schedule of permissions for material releases and the common parts. This requires some calculations, all mechanical. The simulator can do this tedious, no-brainer work for us.

Click on the ⊕ icon, the second from left, to get into the scheduling window.

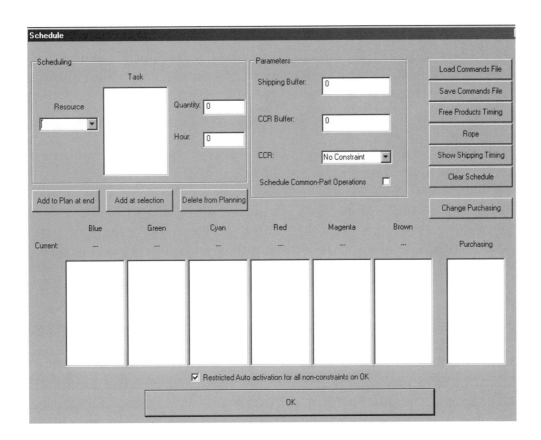

On the left side of the window is the CCR scheduling part. Click on the down-arrow of the 'Resource' field. A list of all the resources will show up, then choose the 'Blue', which is the first on the list. Once you have clicked on the Blue, all the Blue operations would show at the 'Task' list. Click on B6., then on the 'Quantity' field and type 23. DO NOT ENTER ANY HOUR. Just click now on 'Add to Plan at end', and the instruction would appear in the Blue column.

Now click on C6, at the 'Task' and put 15 units at the quantity field and then click 'Add to Plan at end'. Continue to enter the above schedule.

If after you have clicked on 'Add to Plan at end' you like to change the instruction, then mark the instruction and click on 'Delete from Planning'. Then use the Task and Quantity fields to enter the right data and then click on 'Add at selection' to return the updated instruction into its proper place.

Now you need to fill in the identity of the constraint and the appropriate buffers. Go to the 'Parameters' section of the scheduling window. Put 10 for the constraint buffer, and 20 for the shipping buffer. Click on the down-arrow for the 'Constraint' field and then click on Blue.

Now mark the box at 'Schedule common-part operations'. And now click on the 'Rope' button at the right side of the window.

In the 'Purchasing' column you see the resulting schedule of material release. Verify the quantities and time. The common parts permissions schedule for the brown and cyan resources also appears. Verify them as well.

If you are unclear about the process for entering the schedule instructions for a CCR, click on 'Load Commands File' and chose 'Commands.960'.

If you'd like to save your own schedule, then click on 'Save Commands File'. When you give the file name make sure the name is 'commands.' and then add a three digit number that do not clash with existing files.

Now click on OK. Leave the box 'Restricted Auto activation on all non-constraints on OK' marked.
Click the Freeze key to start the clock and watch how smoothly the plant runs itself. If you are bored, you can increase the pace using the '+' icon.

Run the simulator again, to prove to yourself to what extent breakdowns are not the real factor and that what is important is not so much the sequence of the drum but the fact that we operate according to DBR. This time, after you call for plant 360, go to the scheduling window and load 'Commands.961'. When the instruction screen appears you will see that this time we have entered the exact opposite sequence. You'd need to fill in the buffers and constraint's identity, mark the common part box and run Rope. Then re-run the simulation.

V-shape and A-shape plants are very different from each other. Nevertheless, DBR and Buffer Management are implemented in exactly the same way and lead to the same delightful jump in performance.

Now let's examine another, very different shape, the T-shape industries. To those industries belong most of the electronic industries, the car industry as a whole and less high-tech industries, like faucets.

Activate the simulator on plant 390 ('params.390), and examine the nightmare which appears on the screen:

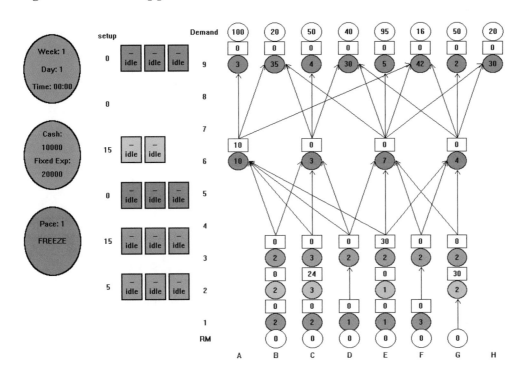

At the bottom we see the tasks needed to produce parts. The red tasks are assembly operations requiring several parts, many of which are common to more than one assembly. For example, assembly C6 requires parts B, C and D, while assembly E6 requires parts D, E, F and G. The next level, done by the Blue resource can deal with an individual sub assembly or create a major assembly. For example, task A9 requires only A6, but B9 is an assembly of A6, C6 and E6.

In an actual T-plant the number of sub-assemblies and final assemblies are by far bigger than the number of parts. The lead time of the assembly operations is much shorter than the lead time to produce the parts. This results in the shape of a T. The problem in this industry is that assembly departments strive for high efficiencies. (For example, in the car industry, stopping the assembly line is equivalent to a major crime.)

Now put yourself in the shoes of a foreman in charge of an assembly department–the Red or the Blue resources. In order to produce E6 you need D, E, F and G. Suppose part D is not available now, you cannot assemble E6. You raise hell about its unavailability, which puts pressure on the Magenta foreman to produce more Ds, and in the meantime you assemble G6. You have the parts for that assembly (verify this). At last, part D arrives. But now, due to the fact that you assembled G6 you ran out of part F. You put the pressure on the Magenta foreman to produce F. But this doesn't help right now, you still cannot assemble E6. However, having parts B, C and D you can assemble C6. Since you are under the gun to score high efficiencies, you do it.

Finally, part F arrives. But because you have assembled C6, you are once again out of part D. At this point assembly E6 is very late. You put tremendous pressure on the Magenta foreman to supply D. He doesn't like it one bit–he just supplied you with D and now you want more! Urgently! Learning from this hard experience he will disregard the quantity you request and produce D in a much larger batch. Which will, of course, increase the lead time. You see the result? Wrong assemblies are produced, inventories are through the roof, due date performance is terrible, and batch sizes in production are out of proportion.

To cope, these industries have enlarged and enlarged and enlarged their capacity. Usually they have a lot of excess capacity – there are no CCRs. What is needed is the simplest implementation of Drum-Buffer-Rope. The only constraint is the market demand. Assembly should be restricted to assemble only what is needed for the very short horizon. Batches in production should be cut drastically.

Click on the 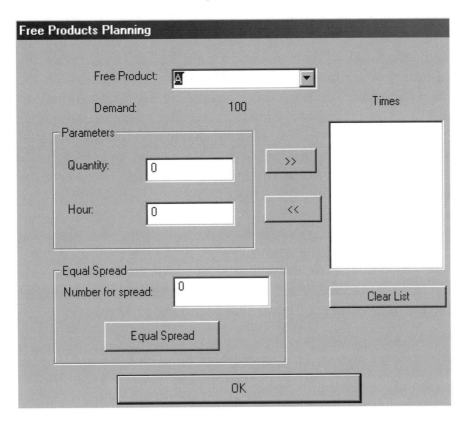 icon, the second from left, to get into the scheduling window. Now click on the 'Free Products Timing' button on the right side of the window. You'll get the following window:

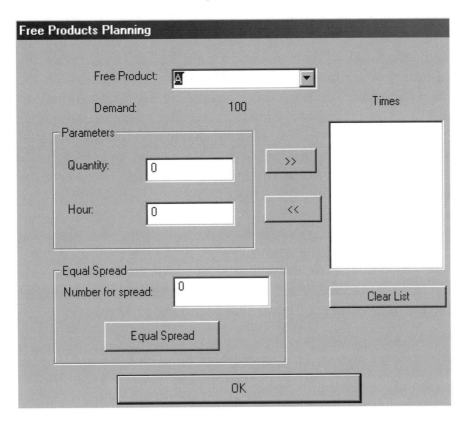

As no constraint has been defined, all the products are considered 'free products'. For each product, starting with A (which already appears at the top of the window) go to the part at the bottom called 'Equal Spread'. Put 1 on the field 'Number for spread' and click on 'Equal Spread'. When you do it the schedule: 100 units to be shipped on hour 40.

For the time being don't click on OK. Instead continue by clicking on the down-arrow of the field 'Free Product' at the top and choose 'B'. Repeat the same procedure. Repeat for all the products. At the end, after entering product H to be shipped on hour 40, click OK on the Free Products Planning to close the window.

Important advice, click on the 'Show Shipping Timing' to check that all the products have one shipping instruction - to ship at hour 40.

You still need to enter the shipping buffer size. As you have asked for all products to be shipped by hour 40, you had better choose the shipping buffer to be 40 hours or no material will be released at the beginning of the week. Type your shipping buffer size (ignore the constraint buffer) and mark the Common-part box. Then click on the Rope button. Don't bother to save your planning. Run the simulator. You would need to return some materials in order to have cash to buy the materials you don't have. You do it by clicking on the raw material circle and put a negative number to purchase. Feel free to activate machines and give purchase instructions if you see fit. Managing the plant is quite a task, but you can score quite well.

Next, let's see what happens when we limit the assembly schedule to a horizon not of one week, but about one day. Restart, following the same actions up to the point where instead of typing 1 for one shipment at the end of the week you will now enter equal spreading in 5 intervals during the week. Repeat that for all the products.

Check again with the 'Show Shipping Timing'. Make sure that each product has five shipping instructions.
You still need to specify the shipping buffer. If we allow at this stage a buffer of say 24 hours, assembly can assemble now for an order three days away. On the other hand, if we make the buffer only 5 hours, production cannot work in the first three hours of each day. So let's choose a buffer of 10 hours. (In reality, the shipping buffer for production should be significantly larger than the shipping buffer for assembly.)

Don't bother to save the planning, just start the run. The plant runs much smoother this time.

You almost cannot exaggerate in cutting the batches and the horizon. Re-run it again, with equal spread of 10 intervals still maintaining a buffer size of ten (parts lead times are longer than assembly lead times). The plant runs even smoother.

When guiding a group, if the organization is an A-shape, don't bother to show V and T plants. If the organization is either V or T-shaped, only at this stage show the corresponding simulator—not before.

18 INTRODUCING DRUM-BUFFER-ROPE AND BUFFER-MANAGEMENT INTO OPERATIONS

Do some preparation work. Make the key people read The Goal or watch The Goal video. Then, of course assuming that the plant manager is behind you, start by addressing all the key managers at the same time. Doing it piece-meal might introduce power struggles that will not help speed up the implementation.

The key people are:
- The superintendents of all shifts, and if in your operation there are important service departments, like maintenance and tool room, the superintendents of these departments as well.
- The top managers of material.
- The controller.
- The chief stewards if you are a union shop.
- The computer wiz of the plant (not of corporate).

Make sure that enough time is allotted–five days (not necessarily consecutive). Order a work book (the appendix of this book) with the simulator for each participant. Copying and Xeroxing is theft. Follow the instructions in this Tutor Guide to the letter. Please do not take any short cuts–they are not short cuts and may block the entire process.

When you have finished bringing them through the material in this book, facilitate a group discussion of how they are going to do it for their operation. Make sure that the discussion follows the five steps:

First, have a consensus on the constraints, or a consensus of the trial constraints that will lead to the accurate identification of the true constraints.

Then, reach a consensus on the mechanism to exploit each constraint–who will provide the information, who will determine the schedule, who authorizes it, etc.

Next, reach consensus on the mechanism of tying the ropes.

Only then, allow the group to have some discussion about elevating the constraint.

At that stage, you are going to be confronted with the third layer of resistance; the "Yes, BUT...". The magnitude of the resistance will be in direct proportion to two factors. One is the quality of the facilitation you have done up to now and the second is the personalities involved.

To answer the "Yes, but..." you must be extremely careful not to allow the dismissal of any "but". Moreover don't allow yourself or others to answer the "buts." Rather you have to take over and clarify exactly the logic–all the cause and effects–behind the "but." Preferably in writing. (Each "yes, but..." is a Negative Branch). You know you have written it well when the person who said "Yes, but..." is the person who after understanding the Negative Branch that you wrote, also suggests the solution. You have to continue doing this until no "Yes, but's" remain and all the attention of the group shifts to obstacles that can block the implementation.

If you are a "Jonah" you know how to handle it systematically. If you have a lot of experience you know how to handle it. If the plant manager is really enthused by what you have taught them up until now, he/she will know how to handle it.

The result should be a detailed implementation plan–what should be done, in what sequence and by whom. Then, for each agreed upon action, write down for the group their answers to three very important questions:

1. What explicit need does the specific action answer?

2. What are the objectives (the expected results) of each specific action?

3. Why do we expect that the specific action will
   answer the specific need to the extent that the
   specific objective will result?

This last step might look redundant but in my experience it is essential.
Otherwise you might not reach a true consensus but an artificial
consensus–each participant having their own, different interpretation
of what was agreed upon.

Once there is a true consensus on the agreed upon action plan, repeat
the education with lower level managers and employees. Do it in
groups of maximum 20, but you don't need five days for each group,
since the plan has been already agreed upon. You need about two
days to bring people to fully jump on the band wagon. Start with the
people directly involved with the constraint and with the people
releasing material. After you have taught them, the actual
implementation starts. Then gradually spread the education until
everybody is included.

If you don't feel that you are in good enough command of this know-
how, or if you have good reasons to suspect strong resistance, don't
risk it. Call an expert for the first round, for the five days with the key
people. After that, to spread it throughout the organization, don't be
afraid to do it yourself, you do know enough.

PRODUCTION THE TOC WAY

WORK BOOK

PART ONE: THE PROBLEM

PART TWO: A SOLUTION

PART ONE: THE PROBLEM

Why is it difficult to manage production?

1. _____

_____

2. _____

_____

3. _____

_____

4. _____

_____

5. _____

_____

6. _____

_____

7. _____

_____

8. _____

_____

For each suggested reason, estimate the feasibility of overcoming it, the cost and the time required:

	Feasibility	Cost	Time
1			
2			
3			
4			
5			
6			
7			
8			

If a major reason is eliminated, the effect it was causing must be significantly reduced.

IF:

Clients never change their mind,
and
vendors always supply, whatever we ask for, on time,
and
we do not have any absenteeism problems with our workforce
and
they are excellently trained and disciplined
and
our processes are reliable
and
our machines never break down
and
our quality is superb
and
data is readily available and accurate
AND
YOU CAN DECIDE ON WHATEVER POLICIES YOU WANT

THEN:

Managing production will be a piece of cake.

BUT: Is it ?!

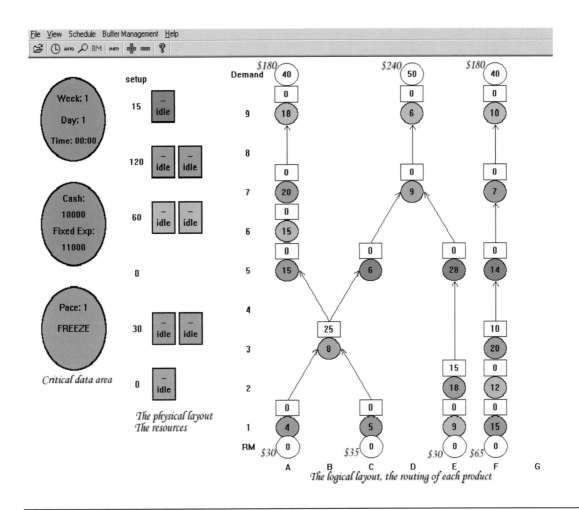

Activate: Click on the machine unit, drag to the task and drop
Purchase: Click on the material circle, then fill in the quantity and OK
Info: Click on the fifth icon from the left – the row just below the menu
Limit: Click on the task, fill in the limit and then click on OK
Auto-Activation: Click on the third icon from the left

Comments:

_____

_____

_____

_____

_____

_____

_____

_____

_____

_____

_____

_____

_____

RUN RESULTS

Financial Results

Net profit _____

Cash _____

Return on investment _____

Throughput _____

Inventory _____

Operating expenses _____

Utilization of resources

Resource	% production	% set up
Blue	_____	_____
Green	_____	_____
Cyan	_____	_____
Magenta	_____	_____
Brown	_____	_____

Order Fulfillment

Product	Quantity required	Quantity delivered
A	_____	_____
D	_____	_____
F	_____	_____

The simulator provides a paradise plant, all external causes were eliminated.
Nevertheless,

was it easy to manage production?

List the undesirable effects you witnessed while running the simulated plant:

1.	
2.	
3.	

In the light of the results we scored in the "Paradise Plant":

What makes production so difficult to manage?

Or in other words:
What is the cause for these undesirable effects?

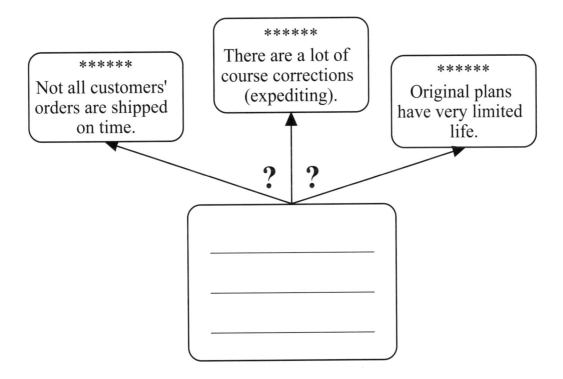

Comments:

_____

_____

_____

_____

_____

_____

_____

_____

_____

_____

_____

_____

_____

_____

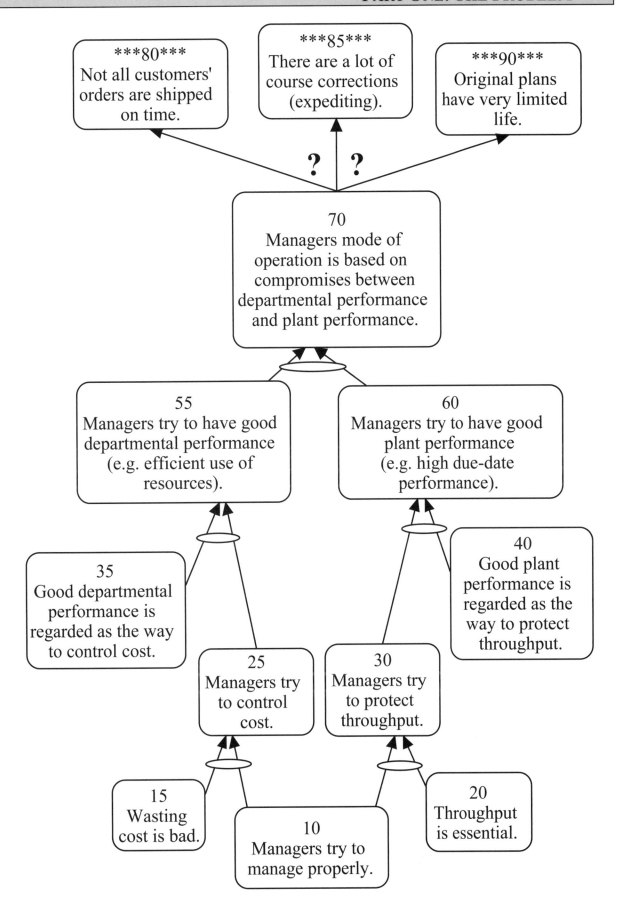

Comments:

_____

_____

_____

_____

_____

_____

_____

_____

_____

_____

_____

_____

_____

1. THE EFFICIENCY SYNDROME:

- "If a worker doesn't have something to do, let's find him something to do!"

- Workers don't want to be caught standing idle.

- Supervisors look for work for their people.

- Managers strive to have high efficiency numbers.

- Corporate will "interfere" if efficiencies are too low.

Run the simulator again assuming that in your plant the efficiency syndrome does exist:

1. Put all resources on auto-activation, the third icon from the left: AUTO . Click on the 'Full' button on the screen.
2. Release enough material to keep everybody busy.
3. Continue releasing material to keep everybody busy.
4. Don't try to reach your efficiency targets by wasting too much time on set-ups. You'll be caught.
5. The green machines are very expensive. If efficiency is too low corporate (the facilitator) will come to "help" you.
6. Still meet your shipping and financial targets.

Comments:

_____

_____

_____

_____

_____

_____

_____

_____

_____

_____

_____

_____

RUN RESULTS WITH EFFICIENCY SYNDROME

Financial Results

Net profit _____

Cash _____

Return on investment _____

Throughput _____

Inventory _____

Operating expenses _____

Utilization of resources

Resource	% production	% set up
Blue	_____	_____
Green	_____	_____
Cyan	_____	_____
Magenta	_____	_____
Brown	_____	_____

Order Fulfillment

Product	Quantity required	Quantity delivered
A	_____	_____
D	_____	_____
F	_____	_____

THE EFFICIENCY SYNDROME:

"IF A WORKER DOESN'T HAVE SOMETHING TO DO, LET'S FIND HIM SOMETHING TO DO!"

The simulator provides a paradise plant, all external causes were eliminated.
Nevertheless,

was it easy to manage production?

List the undesirable effects you witnessed while running the simulated plant:

1.	
2.	
3.	
4.	

Comments:

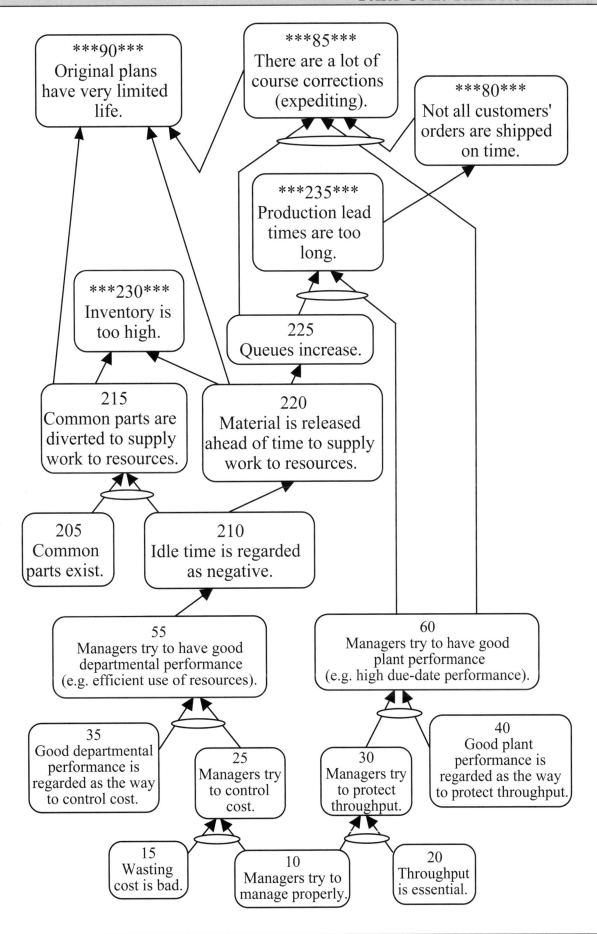

90
Original plans have very limited life.

85
There are a lot of course corrections (expediting).

80
Not all customers' orders are shipped on time.

235
Production lead times are too long.

230
Inventory is too high.

225
Queues increase.

215
Common parts are diverted to supply work to resources.

220
Material is released ahead of time to supply work to resources.

205
Common parts exist.

210
Idle time is regarded as negative.

55
Managers try to have good departmental performance (e.g. efficient use of resources).

60
Managers try to have good plant performance (e.g. high due-date performance).

35
Good departmental performance is regarded as the way to control cost.

25
Managers try to control cost.

30
Managers try to protect throughput.

40
Good plant performance is regarded as the way to protect throughput.

15
Wasting cost is bad.

10
Managers try to manage properly.

20
Throughput is essential.

Comments:

_____

_____

_____

_____

_____

_____

_____

_____

_____

_____

_____

_____

OUR ORGANIZATION IS A CHAIN

COST WORLD

Chain analogy:

Prime measurement - WEIGHT

Any improvement of any link is an improvement of the chain.

GOOD GLOBAL RESULTS = SUM OF GOOD LOCAL RESULTS.

THROUGHPUT WORLD

Chain analogy:

Prime measurement - STRENGTH

Most improvements of most links do not improve the chain.

GOOD GLOBAL RESULTS • SUM OF GOOD LOCAL RESULTS.

Comments:

_____

_____

_____

_____

_____

_____

_____

_____

_____

_____

_____

_____

_____

_____

Comments:

_____

_____

_____

_____

_____

_____

_____

_____

_____

_____

_____

_____

_____

_____

BATCH SIZE DILEMMA IN THE COST WORLD

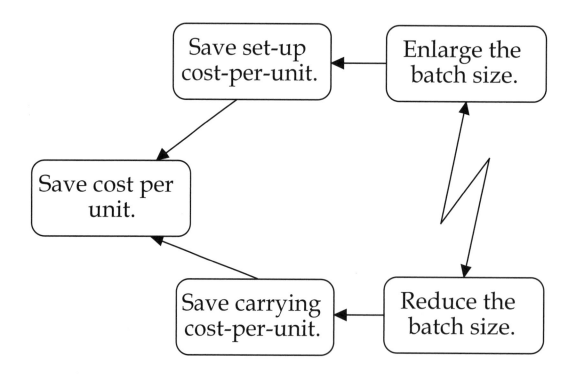

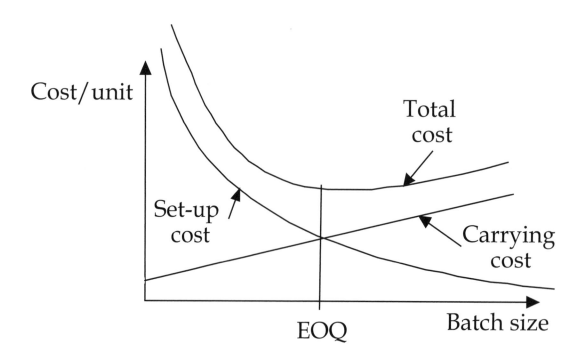

2. THE BATCH SIZE SYNDROME:

Local optima per resource -
"WHAT DO YOU MEAN SPENDING TWO HOURS ON SET-
UP AND THEN PRODUCING FOR ONLY HALF AN HOUR?"

Local optima per product -
"HOW CAN WE MAINTAIN CONTROL IF WE KEEP-ON
SPLITTING WORK ORDERS?"

Work orders are cut for "reasonable" quantities.

Workers are not allowed to pull partial work orders.

Run simulation 312. In your plant the work-order quantities are now set to always be 20 units.

1. Choose whether or not to put resources on Auto-activation. You may change this decision throughout the run.

2. Only you can decide to deviate from the instruction to always maintain the integrity of a work order. Click on the task and mark the box 'One-Time Override Batch'.

3. In your plant everyone is trying to maintain the integrity of the work orders. Therefore if you want to expedite quantities smaller than 20 you have to give the appropriate instruction at each stage separately.

4. To use residual work-in-progress you may complete the work order quantity by expediting units from raw materials.

Comments:

_____

_____

_____

_____

_____

_____

_____

_____

_____

_____

_____

_____

_____

_____

RUN RESULTS WITH
BATCH-SIZE SYNDROME

Financial Results

Net profit	_____
Cash	_____
Return on investment	_____
Throughput	_____
Inventory	_____
Operating expenses	_____

Utilization of resources

Resource	% production	% set up
Blue	_____	_____
Green	_____	_____
Cyan	_____	_____
Magenta	_____	_____
Brown	_____	_____

Order Fulfillment

Product	Quantity required	Quantity delivered
A	_____	_____
D	_____	_____
F	_____	_____

Comments:

_____

_____

_____

_____

_____

_____

_____

_____

_____

_____

_____

_____

_____

_____

_____

_____

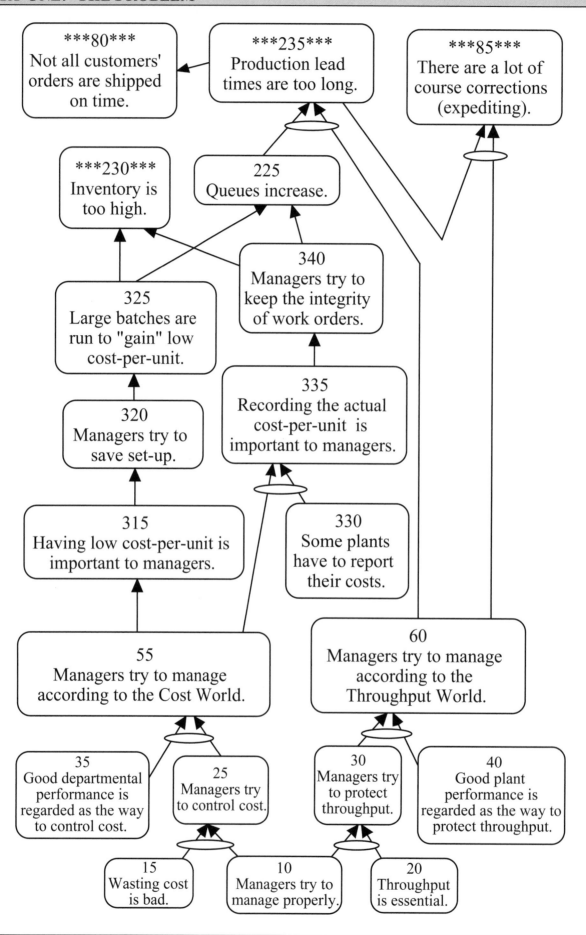

80
Not all customers' orders are shipped on time.

235
Production lead times are too long.

85
There are a lot of course corrections (expediting).

230
Inventory is too high.

225
Queues increase.

340
Managers try to keep the integrity of work orders.

325
Large batches are run to "gain" low cost-per-unit.

335
Recording the actual cost-per-unit is important to managers.

320
Managers try to save set-up.

315
Having low cost-per-unit is important to managers.

330
Some plants have to report their costs.

55
Managers try to manage according to the Cost World.

60
Managers try to manage according to the Throughput World.

35
Good departmental performance is regarded as the way to control cost.

25
Managers try to control cost.

30
Managers try to protect throughput.

40
Good plant performance is regarded as the way to protect throughput.

15
Wasting cost is bad.

10
Managers try to manage properly.

20
Throughput is essential.

Comments:

_____

_____

_____

_____

_____

_____

_____

_____

_____

_____

_____

_____

_____

_____

_____

WHAT ABOUT THE ORIGINAL LIST OF CAUSES?

THEY ADD FUEL TO THE ALREADY EXISTING FIRE!

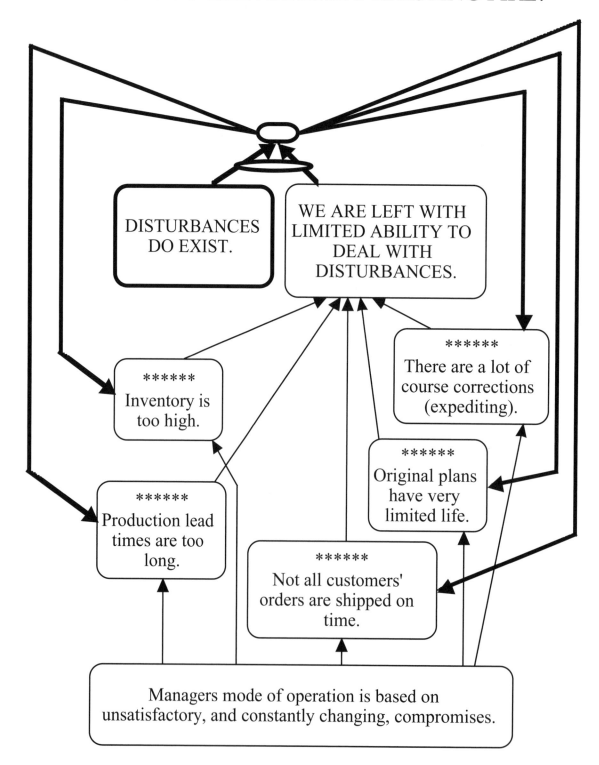

Summary:

_____

_____

_____

_____

_____

_____

_____

_____

_____

_____

_____

_____

_____

_____

_____

_____

_____

_____

_____

_____

_____

_____

_____

_____

WE HAVE MET THE

ENEMY.

IT IS US!

PART TWO: THE SOLUTION

ASSUMPTIONS UNDERLYING
THE BASIC DILEMMA

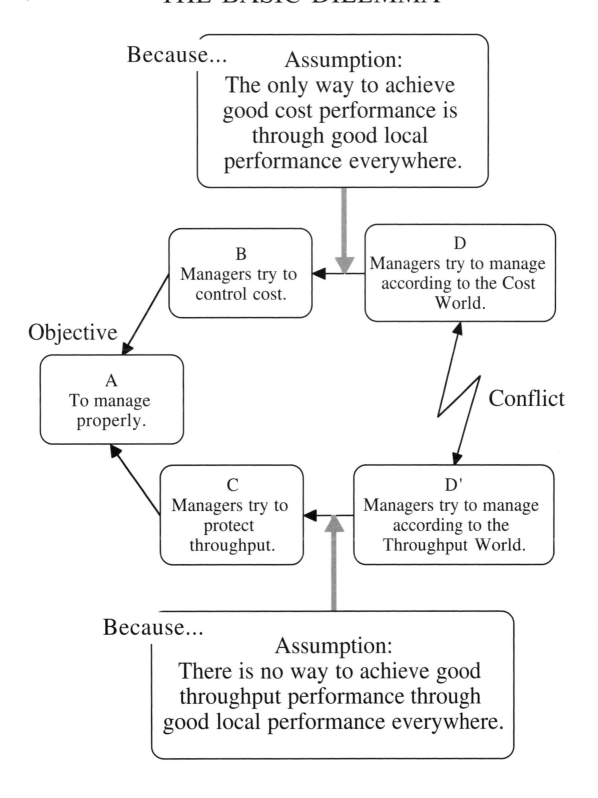

Because...

Assumption:
The only way to achieve good cost performance is through good local performance everywhere.

B
Managers try to control cost.

D
Managers try to manage according to the Cost World.

Objective

A
To manage properly.

Conflict

C
Managers try to protect throughput.

D'
Managers try to manage according to the Throughput World.

Because...

Assumption:
There is no way to achieve good throughput performance through good local performance everywhere.

Compare your first simulator run - your first plant, to the second run - your second plant where you tried to achieve high efficiencies.

QUESTIONS:

1. In which plant did you ship more goods to the market?

2. In which plant were the resources more loaded?

In light of the answers:
3. In which plant is there more pressure to hire and/or to buy more resources?

In light of the answer:
4. In which plant will costs be more under control?

QUESTIONS:

1. In which plant was there more inventory at the end of the week?

2. If you yield to the pressure and add resources, in which plant would the impact on resulting inventory be bigger?

In light of the answers:
3. In which plant are costs more under control?

What do you think about the assumption:

The only way to achieve good cost performance is through good local performance everywhere?

Comments:

_____

_____

_____

_____

_____

_____

_____

_____

_____

_____

_____

THERE IS NO CONFLICT!

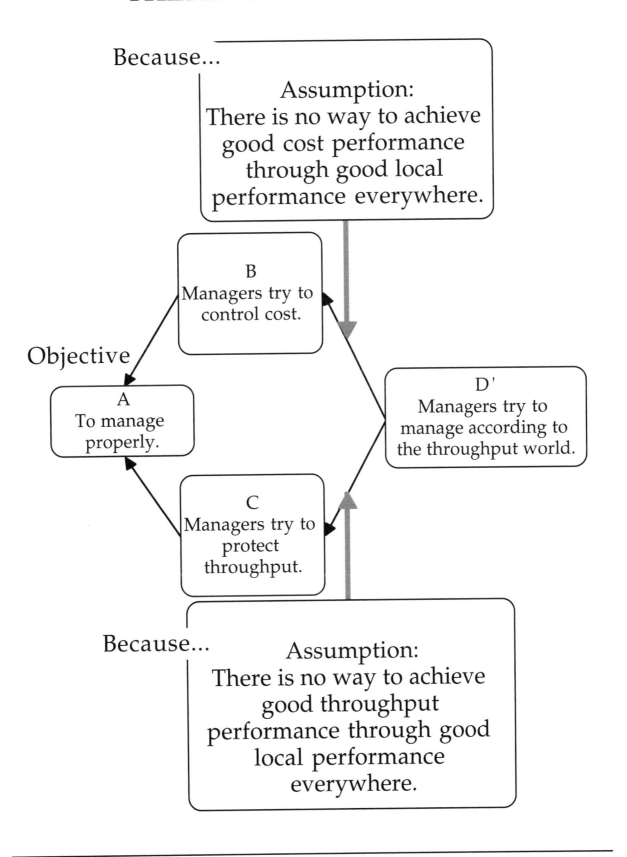

Because...

Assumption:
There is no way to achieve good cost performance through good local performance everywhere.

B
Managers try to control cost.

Objective

A
To manage properly.

D'
Managers try to manage according to the throughput world.

C
Managers try to protect throughput.

Because...

Assumption:
There is no way to achieve good throughput performance through good local performance everywhere.

Comments:

_____

_____

_____

_____

_____

_____

_____

_____

_____

_____

_____

Some throughput world questions about the batch size dilemma in the cost world:

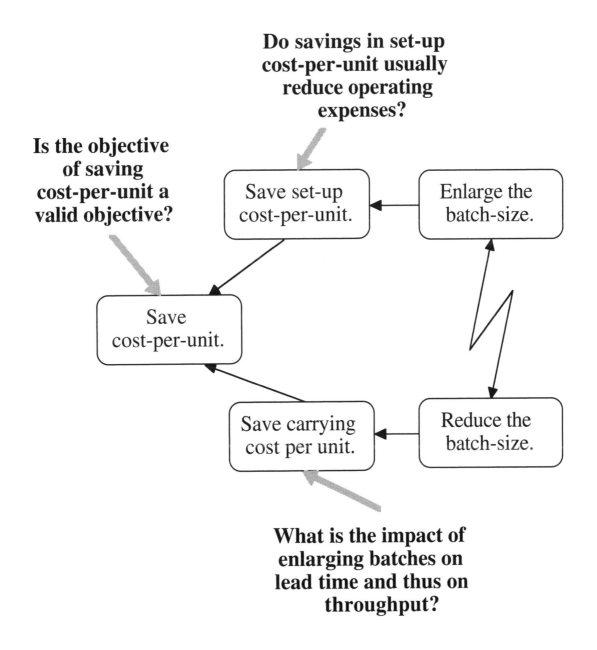

Do savings in set-up cost-per-unit usually reduce operating expenses?

Is the objective of saving cost-per-unit a valid objective?

Save set-up cost-per-unit.

Enlarge the batch-size.

Save cost-per-unit.

Save carrying cost per unit.

Reduce the batch-size.

What is the impact of enlarging batches on lead time and thus on throughput?

Comments:

_____

_____

_____

_____

_____

_____

_____

_____

_____

_____

THE BATCH SIZE DILEMMA IN THE THROUGHPUT WORLD

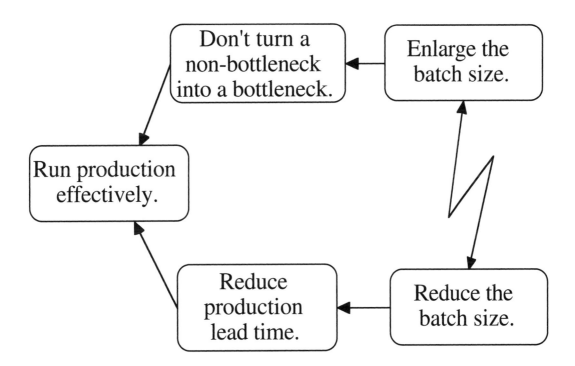

Questions that might help us to break out of the box:

1. Compare your first simulator run to your third run. In which did you get better results?

2. Compare the average batch sizes that you intuitively used in the first run to the avarage batches that you used in the third. Was there any significant difference in the average batch sizes?

3. What difference in the way you handled batches can explain the difference between the results of the two runs?

What is the batch size in a transfer line dedicated to a specific product?

Answer:

Are you sure? Try again.

Alternative Answer:

Both answers are right. How can it be?

Comments:

_____

_____

_____

_____

_____

_____

_____

_____

_____

_____

No BATCH SIZE DILEMMA
IN THE THROUGHPUT WORLD

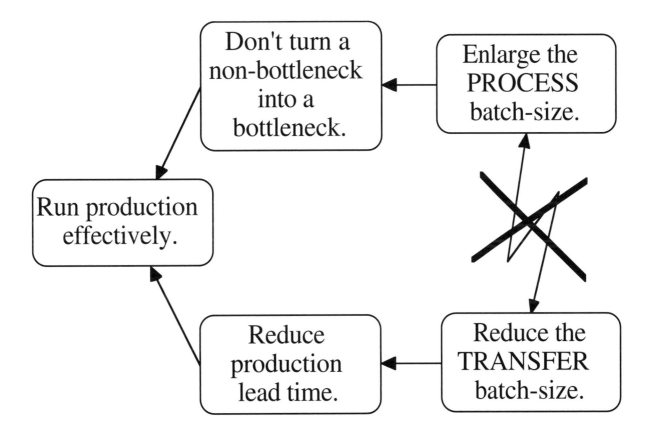

And what should we do about control?

And what about the necessary paperwork?

Comments:

_____

_____

_____

_____

_____

_____

_____

_____

_____

_____

THE PROCESS

STEP 1: IDENTIFY the system's constraint(s).

STEP 2: Decide how to EXPLOIT the system's constraint(s).

STEP 3: SUBORDINATE everything else to the above decision.

STEP 4: ELEVATE the system's constraint(s).

STEP 5: If in a previous step a constraint has been broken, go back to step 1, but do not allow INERTIA to cause a system's constraint.

STEP 1: IDENTIFY the system's constraint(s).

In the simulated Paradise plant, what are the system's constraints?

1.
2.

What is the system's constraint in the simulated plant the way we ran it the second time?

What is the system's constraint in the simulated plant the way we ran it the third time?

STEP 2: Decide how to EXPLOIT the system's constraint(s).

For the capacity constraint resource, we decide, in advance, how we are going to use its scarce capacity. We decide in detail, reserving improvization for emergencies.

Decide on the schedule for the Blue resource:

	Operation	Quantity
1.	_____	_____
2.	_____	_____
3.	_____	_____
4.	_____	_____
5.	_____	_____
6.	_____	_____

STEP 3: <u>SUBORDINATE</u> everything else to the above decision.

The efficiency syndrome is still alive and kicking on the shop floor. For decades we hammered efficiencies into our work force; always being busy has become the work ethic.

What is the work ethic that we should institute in its place?

THE "ROAD RUNNER" WORK ETHIC

Beep, beep.

<u>First on the simulated plant</u>

1. We identified the system's constraints:
They are the Blue resource and the market demand for product A - the free product.

2. We decided how to exploit the constraints:
The Blue resource schedule has been set to guarantee satisfying the market demand. We are going to pay particular attention that the Blue resource will follow this schedule without hic-ups. And we are not going to forget satisfying the market for the free product.

3. We are going to subordinate everything else to the above decisions:
   • All resources will be on auto-activation (without permission to use common parts).
   • We are not going to complicate our life with artificial work-orders.
   • Above all, our attention will be on the Blue resource and the free product, A.

4. We are not yet going to take any actions to elevate the constraints since we don't know if the Blue resource will continue to be a constraint and we are not from marketing.

Why do we expect performance to improve?!

Comments:

Here's why:

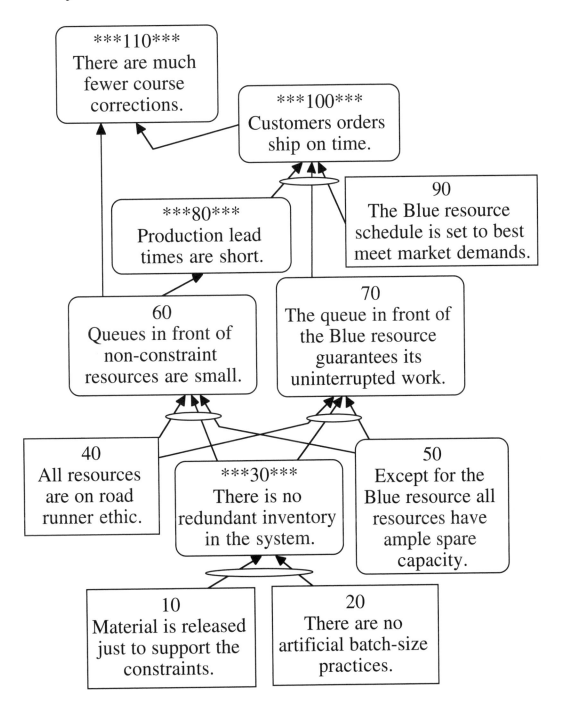

Comments:

_____

_____

_____

_____

_____

_____

_____

_____

_____

_____

Let's try it. Decide on the schedules for the constraints:

Blue resource schedule

	Operation	Quantity
1.	_____	_____
2.	_____	_____
3.	_____	_____
4.	_____	_____
5.	_____	_____
6.	_____	_____

Shipping schedule for product A

	Day	Quantity
1.	_____	_____
2.	_____	_____

RUN RESULTS

Financial Results
Net Profit:
Cash:
Return on Investment:
Throughput:
Inventory:
Operating Expenses:

Utilization of Resources		
	% Production	% Set Up
Blue		
Green		
Cyan		
Magenta		
Brown		

Order Fulfillment		
Product	Quantity Required	Quantity Delivered
A		
D		
F		

It worked! But not perfectly.

What still went wrong? And why?

1.

2.

3.

Comments:

_____

_____

_____

_____

_____

_____

_____

_____

_____

_____

An explanation for the emergence of negative effects:

A NEGATIVE BRANCH

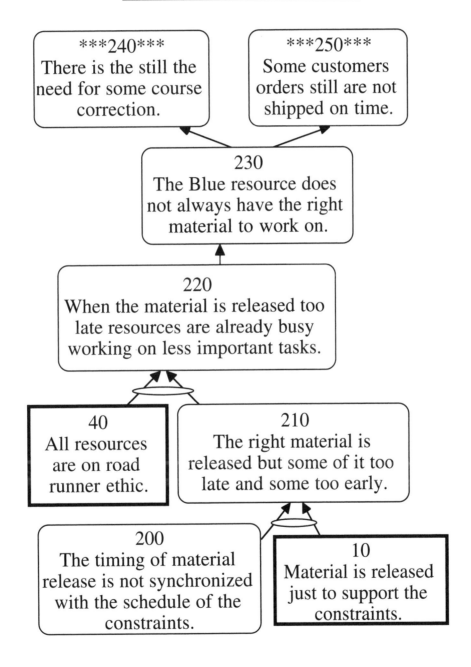

240
There is the still the need for some course correction.

250
Some customers orders still are not shipped on time.

230
The Blue resource does not always have the right material to work on.

220
When the material is released too late resources are already busy working on less important tasks.

40
All resources are on road runner ethic.

210
The right material is released but some of it too late and some too early.

200
The timing of material release is not synchronized with the schedule of the constraints.

10
Material is released just to support the constraints.

Comments:

_____

_____

_____

_____

_____

_____

_____

_____

_____

_____

THE BOY SCOUT ANALOGY

W.I.P.

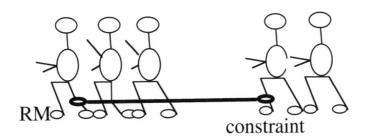

RM

constraint

Comments:

_____

_____

_____

_____

_____

_____

_____

_____

_____

_____

_____

Drum-Buffer-Rope
DBR

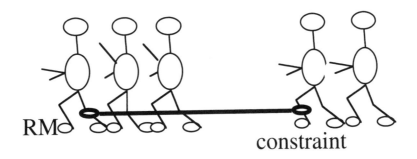

RM

constraint

Transferring the lesson to production:

1. _____
_____
_____
_____
_____

2. _____
_____
_____
_____
_____

Shipping Buffer Time = 20 Hours.
CCR Buffer time = 10 Hours

Blue Resource Schedule

Material Release Schedule

	Operation	Quantity	Approx. Starting time	Raw Material	Quantity	Time
1.	F5	10	00:00	-	-	-
2.	E5	15	02:	-	-	-
3.	C5	15	10:	-	-	-
4.	F5	30	12:	F	30	2:
5.	C5	35	20:	A,C	35, 35	10:
6.	E5	35	23:	E	35	13:

Product A Shipping schedule

	Day	Quantity	Start time	Raw Material	Quantity	Time
1.	1	10	16:	-	-	-
2.	4	30	32:	A,C	30, 30	12:

SHIPPING BUFFER TIME = _____ HOURS
CCR BUFFER TIME = _____ HOURS

Blue Resource Schedule

Material Release Schedule

	Operation	Quantity	Approximate Starting Time	Raw Material	Quantity	Time
1.						
2.						
3.						
4.						
5.						
6.						

Product A
SHIPPING SCHEDULE

	Day	Quantity	Start	RM	Quantity	Time
1.						
2.						

Comments:

_____

_____

_____

_____

_____

_____

_____

_____

_____

_____

Another Negative Branch:

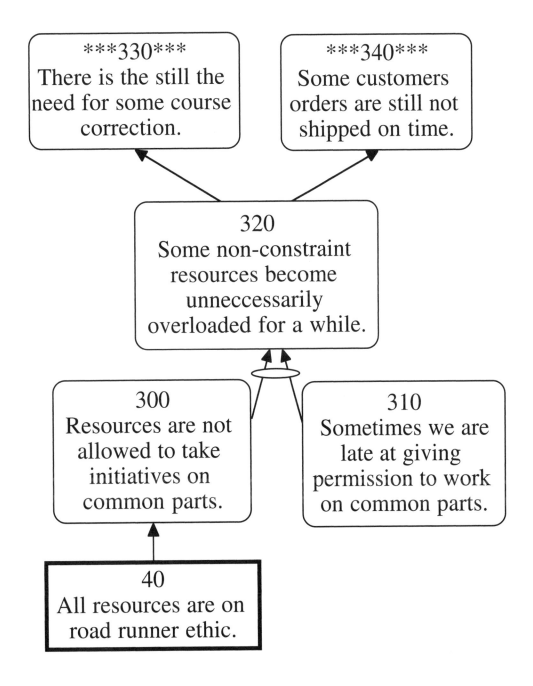

330
There is the still the need for some course correction.

340
Some customers orders are still not shipped on time.

320
Some non-constraint resources become unneccessarily overloaded for a while.

300
Resources are not allowed to take initiatives on common parts.

310
Sometimes we are late at giving permission to work on common parts.

40
All resources are on road runner ethic.

Comments:

_____

_____

_____

_____

_____

_____

_____

_____

_____

_____

RUN RESULTS

Financial Results
Net Profit:
Cash:
Return on Investment:
Throughput:
Inventory:
Operating Expenses:

Utilization of Resources		
	% Production	% Set Up
Blue		
Green		
Cyan		
Magenta		
Brown		

Order Fulfillment		
Product	Quantity Required	Quantity Delivered
A		
D		
F		

NOT BAD.

But why do we need to give the instructions on-line?

Let's give:
- The material release schedule to the people who are responsible for it;
- The schedule of the Blue resource to the person in charge of that work center;
- The schedule of permission to work on common parts to the person in charge of the relevant work center.

This will leave us with nothing to do. So, before we try again, let's discuss:

CONTROL.

In the real world Murphy does exist. What do we have to carefully watch in order to be on top of things?

———————————————————————————

———————————————————————————

———————————————————————————

———————————————————————————

———————————————————————————

RUN RESULTS

Financial Results
Net Profit:
Cash:
Return on Investment:
Throughput:
Inventory:
Operating Expenses:

Utilization of Resources		
	% Production	% Set Up
Blue		
Green		
Cyan		
Magenta		
Brown		

Order Fulfillment		
Product	Quantity Required	Quantity Delivered
A		
D		
F		

Comments:

_____

_____

_____

_____

_____

_____

_____

_____

_____

_____

Exercising buffer content

CCR schedule

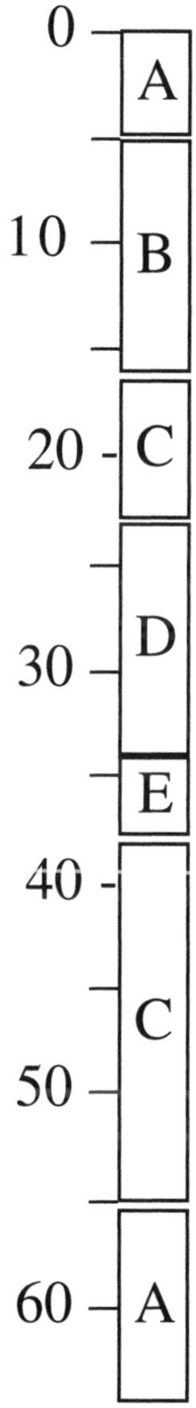

The buffer is 15 hours.

Current time	Region I tasks	Buffer tasks
0	A	A,B
5	B	B,C
10	—	—
15	—	—
20	—	—
25	—	—
30	—	—
35	—	—
40	—	—
45	—	—
50	—	—

CCR schedule column (vertical scale):

0 — A
10 — B
20 — C
30 — D
E
40 — C
50
60 — A

In the previous example, suppose that a non-constraint (feeding the CCR) breaks down, and stays down, when it processes E .

At what time does task E become a HOLE in region III?

At what time in region II?

At what time in region I?

At what time does it penetrate through region I?

A change in the mix of the orders has changed the Capacity Constraint Resource.

• Suppose the new CCR is feeding the old CCR. What will be the impact on both the buffers?

_____

_____

_____

_____

_____

• Suppose the new CCR is not feeding the old CCR. What will be the impact on both the buffers?

_____

_____

_____

_____

_____

Comments:

_____

_____

_____

_____

_____

_____

_____

_____

_____

_____

_____

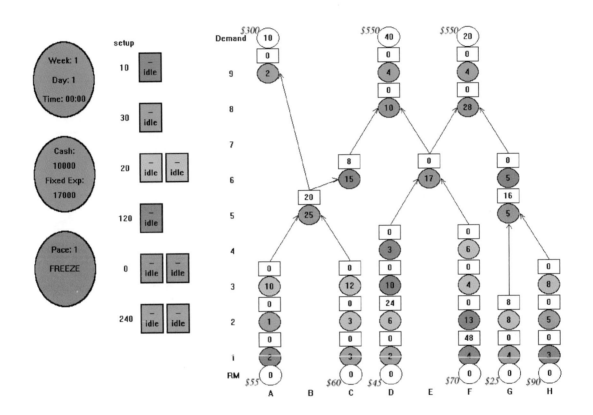

Simulation 350

Comments:

_____

_____

_____

_____

_____

_____

_____

_____

_____

_____

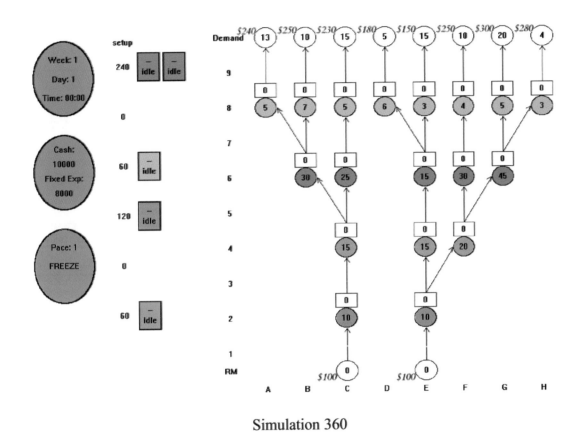

Simulation 360

Comments:

_____

_____

_____

_____

_____

_____

_____

_____

_____

_____

_____

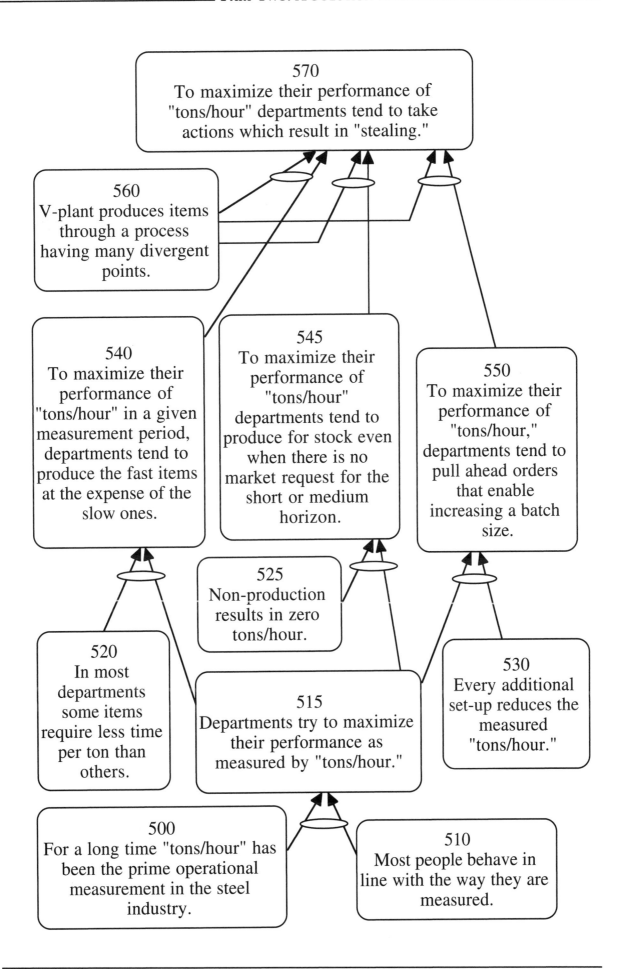

Comments:

_____

_____

_____

_____

_____

_____

_____

_____

_____

_____

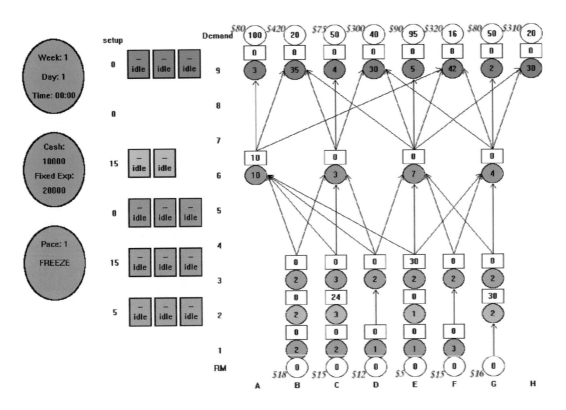

Simulation 390

Comments:

_____

_____

_____

_____

_____

_____

_____

_____

_____

_____

Summary:

_____

_____

_____

_____

_____

_____

_____

_____

_____

_____

For more information on this book and
THE THEORY OF CONTRAINTS (TOC)
please visit Eli Goldratt's web site at
www.eligoldratt.com